JASON EXPEDITION:
Mysteries of Earth and Mars

STUDENT
Activities

JASON Student Host Katie Keller
JASON Host Researcher Kobie Boykins
Mars Yard, NASA Jet Propulsion Laboratory

JASON
FOUNDATION
for EDUCATION

JASON FOUNDATION FOR EDUCATION

JASON Expeditions Team

Tim Armour, *Executive Vice President*

Laura Batt, *Content Producer/Writer*

Ben Carlisle, *Multimedia Content Manager*

Francesca Casella, Ph.D., *Standards and Assessment*

Katie James, *Vice President*

Philip Lanza, *Production Manager*

Susan Richmond, *Content Producer/Writer Consultant*

Josh Sheldon, *Senior Content Producer/Writer*

Additional thanks to

Andrew Amster, *JFE*

Carrie Cowan, *Graphic and Web Design Consultant*

Caroline Joyce, Ph.D., *JFE*

Emily Lu, *Writer/Consultant*

Henry F. Olds, Jr., Ed.D., *JFE*

Haris Papamichael, Ph.D., *JFE*

Elsie Rivard, *JFE*

Joe Walters, *Writer/Consultant*

CONQUEST DESIGN, INC.

Carroll Conquest, *Principal & Creative Director*

Elizabeth Hargreaves, *Graphic Designer*

Jessica Jones, *Graphic Designer*

Additional thanks to

Andrea Golden

Dawn Handley

Matt Mayerchak

Earl Misquitta

BROWN PUBLISHING NETWORK

Linda Vahey, *Editorial Director*

Pam Hirschfeld, *Executive Editor*

Main front and back cover photos by Daniel J. Splaine.

Table of Contents

(3) UNIT 3 LIFE SCIENCE 82

©2006 JASON Foundation for Education

Join the Expedition!
A Letter from Dr. Robert Ballard

JASON Explorers,

Welcome to this year's JASON Expedition, where we will explore our fascinating sister planet, Mars! In 1997, the nation watched in awe as pictures from the first rover, Sojourner, were beamed back to Earth. The Martian landscape came into close view, as strikingly real as the world right here beneath your feet. Since then, there have been many unmanned missions to Mars using satellites and rovers as our eyes and hands. There is even a plan to send humans to Mars within your lifetime!

During *JASON Expedition: Mysteries of Earth and Mars,* you will work alongside our JASON host researchers as they:

- design and build spacecraft to explore Mars.

- compare and contrast the history and geology of Earth and Mars.

- study extreme places and life forms on Earth to gain insight into possible life on Mars.

I've always been intrigued by outer space—though you may know me best as an ocean explorer, and for the discoveries of *Titanic* and deep-sea hydrothermal vents. In fact, ocean exploration and space exploration actually have a lot in common. Both are very important, and both present the challenge of reaching and observing extreme environments—places we can't always go to in person. So as scientists, we have to be very imaginative about the tools that we design and build to do our research. I am using remotely operated vehicles to study deep-sea hydrothermal vents, in much the same way NASA uses rovers to explore Mars.

In this Expedition, you will work as an explorer, often using what you learn about the world around you to answer questions about a world tens of millions of kilometers away. One of the big questions scientists are asking is whether there is now, or ever was, life on Mars. Little by little, scientists are piecing together clues to help answer this and other important questions about our neighboring planet. Most of that research looks at things right here on Earth, including deep-sea environments and their unique life forms, and other extreme environments like deserts and hot springs—places that might be very near to where you live.

It is likely that, as a result of this Expedition, you will be asking many new questions. That's the nature of science. I encourage you to be curious, observant, and imaginative about the world around you and about worlds beyond! Perhaps the research questions you develop today as part of this JASON Expedition will inspire the hypotheses you test in the future as an actual space explorer on a manned mission to Mars!

Now, get ready for a far-out expedition to study the mysteries of Earth and Mars!

Dr. Robert D. Ballard
Founder and Chief Scientist
JASON Foundation for Education

No matter what expedition we're on, we'll look for answers to three important questions:
- **What are the dynamic systems of Earth and space?**
- **How do these systems affect life?**
- **What technologies do we use to study these systems, and why?**

Introduction to
Mysteries of Earth and Mars

Here's a challenge: take a look at the two pictures on this page. One is a photograph of a landscape here on Earth. The other is a picture of the surface of Mars. Can you tell which is which?

For humans, Mars has always been a source of mysteries. For thousands of years, we've looked at this planet, a red point of light in the night sky, and we've wondered: Is it like Earth? Is there life on Mars? Until recently, humans have had no way of answering these questions. But over the past several years, the National Aeronautics and Space Administration (NASA) has launched a series of robotic missions to Mars in an attempt to finally crack some of the planet's secrets.

Every day, spacecraft have circled Mars from above, taking photographs and making detailed measurements. In 2004, NASA landed two robotic rovers on Mars to give us an up-close look at the planet. Spirit and Opportunity, named by a nine-year-old student, explored the nooks and crannies of the Martian surface and made an amazing discovery: that liquid water, a key ingredient for life, once covered parts of Mars.

These missions have confirmed that modern Mars is very different from Earth: it is a cold, dry, desert-like planet with no obvious signs of life. Yet the findings of these missions also hint that Mars and Earth were once much more alike. In this JASON Expedition, we will compare Earth and Mars in our own attempt to investigate the mysteries of both planets. Our adventure will stretch from the deserts of Earth all the way to the volcanoes of Mars. By comparing Earth and Mars, we can discover important things about the nature and history of both planets.

Where are Earth and Mars in the solar system?

Earth and Mars share a history that goes back 4.6 billion years, to the birth of our solar system. A **solar system** is a collection of objects that revolve around a star. Our solar system is made up of the Sun and all of the bodies that revolve around it, including the nine planets, their moons, and various smaller bodies such as asteroids and comets.

All objects in the solar system move around the Sun in a circular or elliptical path called an **orbit**. Closest to the Sun are four rocky

Which photograph was taken on Earth? Which was taken on Mars? *See the answer on the bottom of p. 9.*

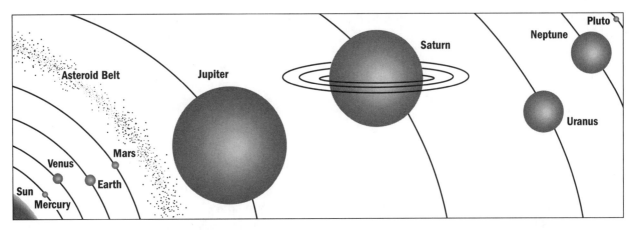

This illustration of our solar system shows the approximate sizes of the planets relative to each other. The distances between the planets are not to scale.

planets: Mercury, Venus, Earth, and Mars. Earth is the third planet from the Sun, traveling at a distance of about 150 million km (93 million mi) in a nearly circular orbit. Mars, the fourth planet from the Sun, moves in a more elliptical path. In its orbit, Mars can get as close to the Sun as 206 million km (128 million mi) or as far away as 249 million km (155 million mi).

Beyond the four rocky planets is a region of the solar system called the **asteroid belt**, where thousands of small rocky and metallic objects orbit the Sun. The remaining planets orbit far beyond the asteroid belt. Four of these—Jupiter, Saturn, Uranus, and Neptune— are known as gas giants, because they are made primarily of gases such as hydrogen and helium, and they are much larger than the rocky planets. The largest gas giant, Jupiter, has a mass 318 times greater than Earth's.

The last planet, Pluto, is an oddball. It is small, rocky, and icy. It is located at the outer edge of the planets, orbiting at an average distance from the Sun of almost 6 billion km (3.7 billion mi).

Our solar system is a very big place. Mars is Earth's neighbor, but it is still incredibly far away. If Earth were the size of a baseball, Mars would be the size of a ping-pong ball more than 300 m (1,000 ft) away.

How do Earth and Mars compare?

Viewed from outer space, Earth and Mars couldn't look more different. Earth has a brilliant blue color, due to the fact that about 70 percent of its surface is covered with liquid water. Mars is reddish brown, a color caused by the presence of iron oxide—also known as rust—in the planet's soil. Mars is also much smaller than Earth. Its diameter is about half of Earth's diameter, and its mass is about one-tenth of Earth's mass.

No human has ever traveled to Mars. But if you could spend a year on Mars' surface, you would notice some obvious differences between Mars and Earth. The most striking difference might be Mars' extreme environmental conditions. Temperatures on Mars average -63 °C (-81 °F)—bitterly cold compared to Earth's average of 14 °C (57 °F). You would notice another difference if you tried to take a breath of Martian air. Just like Earth, Mars has an **atmosphere**, a mixture of gases that surround the planet. But the Martian atmosphere is mostly made up of carbon dioxide, with only traces of the oxygen that makes Earth's air breathable. To survive for even a minute on the surface of Mars, you would need an insulated spacesuit and a supply of oxygen.

With your first steps on Mars, you would find that your body feels lighter there than it does on Earth. This is because the force of gravity on Mars is only 38 percent as strong as the force of gravity on Earth. A person who weighs 40 kg (88 lb) on Earth would weigh only 15 kg (33 lb) on Mars!

Traveling around on Mars' surface, you would notice the complete absence of liquid water—and the complete absence of visible life forms. But you would also see some things that might look familiar to you. For example, Mars and Earth share many geological features, such as dunes, mountains, volcanoes, canyons, craters, and polar ice caps. You would find that Mars' weather can be just as stormy and unpredictable as Earth's, with strong winds and occasional dust storms that can cover the entire planet.

A Martian day, or **sol**, is 39 min longer than a day on Earth. From sunrise to sunrise, Earth takes 24 hr to rotate on its axis, while Mars takes 24 hr and 39 min. But your year on Mars would last nearly twice as long as a year on Earth. Earth takes 365 days to complete a full orbit around the Sun, while Mars takes 687 days, or about 669 sols.

Although it might seem far-fetched to think that you could spend a year on Mars, the idea is actually not that strange. Plans are currently in the works to send a manned mission to Mars within the next 20 years. You might even have a chance to be part of that mission!

What can we learn by studying Earth and Mars?

NASA is not waiting for humans to arrive on Mars to begin answering some of the many questions we have about our sister planet. In fact, thanks to the success of NASA's recent robotic missions, we now know more about Mars than at any point in the past. Yet, for each question answered about Mars, many more questions remain. Why did Mars and Earth evolve in such different ways? Did life

ever arise on Mars? And, if not, why did life flourish on Earth and not on Mars?

In *JASON Expedition: Mysteries of Earth and Mars*, you will work together with leading scientists to tackle these and other questions. Here is a sneak peak at what you'll be doing:

Unit 1: Physical Science

In this unit, you'll investigate the challenges of robotic space exploration with NASA engineers who helped build the latest generation of Mars rovers and orbiters. How do engineers design rovers for the extreme conditions of the Martian surface? How do they plan for the energy needs of an orbiter that will spend five years circling Mars? And what science principles do they use to get these spacecraft from Earth to Mars? As you learn the answers to these questions, you'll have many opportunities to take on design challenges of your own.

Unit 2: Earth and Space Science

For the first billion years of their existence, Earth and Mars were probably very similar. So what caused the differences that we see

JASON host researcher Vicky Hamilton and student host Mitchell Graves examine some rocks in Death Valley, California, a site that is often compared to Mars.

©2006 JASON Foundation for Education

today? In this unit, you'll work along with planetary geologists as they examine the forces that shaped the Martian surface. First, you'll compare the geological processes of Earth and Mars. Then you'll set out to create your own impact craters, analyze a Martian meteorite, and do a side-by-side comparison of your local soil and Martian soil simulant. Be prepared to get your hands dirty!

Unit 3: Life Science

In this unit, you'll join scientists as they investigate the types of life that could survive in the extreme conditions of Mars. You'll find out how to recognize signs of life, and you'll learn about organisms that live in extreme conditions right here on Earth. You'll even have a chance to find out if there are extreme environments in your own neighborhood!

So grab your geologist's kit and your JASON Journal and come along on the *JASON Expedition: Mysteries of Earth and Mars!* As you begin this adventure, create a table in your journal for making your own comparisons of Earth and Mars. Throughout the Expedition, you can use the table to record data, thoughts, musings, research questions, hypotheses, and more.

Comparing Earth and Mars

	Earth	Mars
Age	4.6 billion years	4.6 billion years
Diameter	12,756 km (7,926 mi)	6,794 km (4,222 mi)
Mass (Earth = 1)	1	0.11
Surface Gravity (Earth = 1)	1	0.38
Natural Satellites	Moon	Phobos, Deimos
Distance from the Sun	147–152 million km (91–94 million mi)	206–249 million km (128–155 million mi)
Length of Day	24 hours	24 hours, 39 minutes
Length of Year	365 Earth days	687 Earth days
Average Surface Temperature	14 °C (57 °F)	-63 °C (-81 °F)
Seasons	Yes	Yes
Atmosphere (Main Components)	78% nitrogen 21% oxygen	95% carbon dioxide 3% nitrogen
Tallest Peak	Mt. Everest 8.8 km (5.5 mi)	Olympus Mons 27 km (17 mi)
Deepest Canyon	Cotahuasi Canyon 3 km (2 mi)	Valles Marineris 10 km (6 mi)
Life	Yes	Unknown

Answer to photo challenge: Mars is on the left; Earth is on the right.

©2006 JASON Foundation for Education

Thinking Like a Scientist: How to Design a Scientific Investigation

You may not believe it, but thinking like a scientist is not that hard. Thinking like a scientist begins with making observations and asking questions about the world around you. As part of this JASON Expedition, you will be encouraged to make lots of observations and ask lots of questions. Sometimes you will have a chance to design your own investigation to help answer one of your questions. Scientists follow a series of steps when they design investigations. Here are some steps you can follow to help you think like a scientist as you investigate the mysteries of Earth and Mars.

- **Make detailed observations.** Observations can be qualitative or quantitative. *Qualitative observations* describe qualities such as shape, color, odor, taste, texture, and behavior. *Quantitative observations* describe quantities such as length, mass, temperature, and volume.

- **Ask questions about what you observe.** Based on your observations, ask questions about things that you don't understand or things that you would like to explore in more detail. Select one of your questions to investigate further. This will be your *research question*.

- **Form a hypothesis.** Your *hypothesis* should be an attempt to answer your research question before you conduct your investigation. Your hypothesis must be testable, which means that you must be able to design an investigation that tests whether the hypothesis is true.

- **Design an investigation to test your hypothesis.** To begin, determine what you are testing and how you are going to measure it. Identify your *independent variable*, which is the one factor that you are allowed to vary during your investigation. Then identify your *dependent variable*, which is the factor that you will measure to see how it changes in response to variations in your independent variable. All other factors are *controls* that must be kept the same throughout your investigation. Next, design a step-by-step procedure for your investigation. Include information on how you will vary your independent variable and how you will measure changes in your dependent variable. Also make a list of all the materials you will need for your investigation.

- **Conduct your investigation.** Gather the necessary materials and follow the procedure you have designed.

- **Record data about what happens.** Your *data* are all of the pieces of information you collect while doing your investigation. Be sure to write down everything as it happens!

- **Analyze your data.** After you have completed your investigation, look for patterns in your data and think about whether the patterns support your hypothesis.

- **Draw conclusions.** Write down what you learned from your investigation. Use your data to help you decide whether your hypothesis was supported. Think about other investigations you could do to continue testing your hypothesis.

©2006 JASON Foundation for Education

Map of Mars

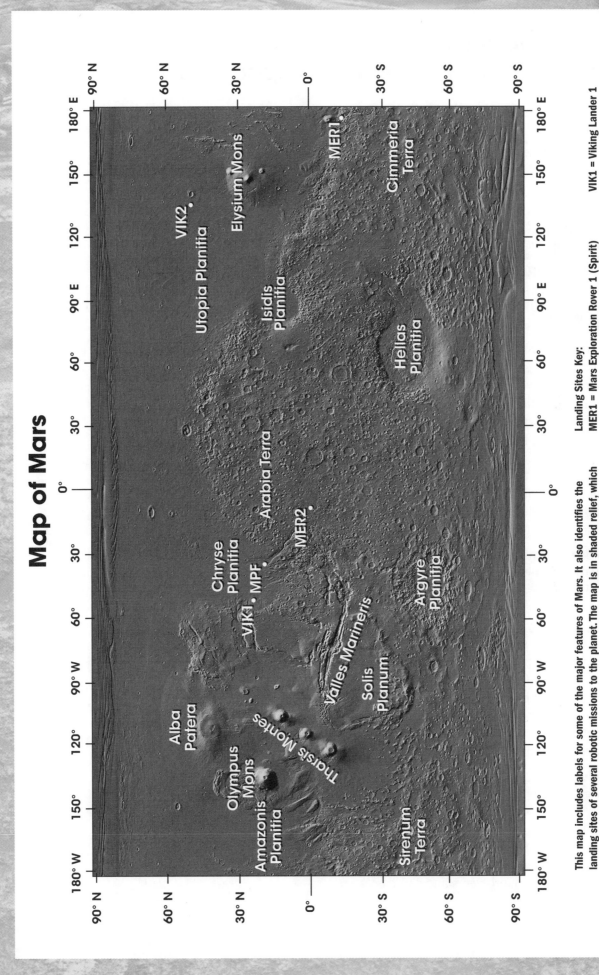

This map includes labels for some of the major features of Mars. It also identifies the landing sites of several robotic missions to the planet. The map is in shaded relief, which means that shadows on the map were drawn as if light were shining on the entire Martian surface from a particular direction. In this case, the surface appears to be illuminated from the upper right.

Landing Sites Key:
MER1 = Mars Exploration Rover 1 (Spirit)
MER2 = Mars Exploration Rover 2 (Opportunity)
MPF = Mars Pathfinder Rover (Sojourner)

VIK1 = Viking Lander 1
VIK2 = Viking Lander 2

Meet the Team for the
Mysteries of Earth and Mars Expedition

UNIT 1 HOST RESEARCHERS

Tracy D. Drain
Systems Engineer
NASA Jet Propulsion
Laboratory, CA

Research Focus:
How do the many systems of the Mars Reconnaissance Orbiter work smoothly together?

Kobie T. Boykins
Senior Mechanical Engineer
NASA Jet Propulsion
Laboratory, CA

Research Focus:
How do engineers build robotic rovers to meet the grueling conditions of Mars?

What inspired you to pursue your career?

I have been interested in space since I was a kid—about eight years old. Sometime around then, I read an article that explained how scientists think the solar system was formed. The idea that the Sun, the planets and their moons, the comets, the asteroids—everything in our "neighborhood"—was formed from one giant cloud of gas billions of years ago was totally stunning to me. Since then, I've been fascinated by everything related to the cosmos.

What would you most like students to learn from participating in this JASON Expedition?

I would love students to get a sense of Mars as a real place, a whole world out there waiting for us. It is not merely a red dot in the sky, too far away to be of any significance. It would be great if students developed an appreciation for what we can learn about our own planet by studying Mars and the rest of the solar system. And I would like to see students get infected with the same enthusiasm that I and many others share for space exploration.

What advice would you give to students who are interested in studying science?

I would advise students to remember that learning is not simply memorizing facts and equations. The most important thing to learn is critical thinking, so that you will be able to think through new types of problems and come up with creative solutions.

How did you end up in the field you are in today?

I entered the field of engineering in no small part because I watched "Star Trek." I know it is a cliché, but I wanted to build interstellar vehicles. Seems that building robotic rovers that explore Mars is the next best thing!

How do you conduct your work and what tools/technology do you use?

To do my work, I use primarily what I have learned in life and what nature teaches us. Mechanical design involves creating a system that works and meets specific requirements. It sounds really easy, but those requirements can produce a very complex set of factors that make a mechanical design almost impossible to achieve. We use computers and anything else we can get our hands on.

What have you learned so far?

I learn more every day. Mars, like Earth, is an amazing planet. It challenges us in every way—from its temperature to its atmosphere. The discovery that water once existed on Mars—wow!—is just awesome. What happened to the water? And, more important to me, could the same thing happen here on Earth? If that isn't a reason to look to the stars and understand what is happening, I don't know what is!

©2006 JASON Foundation for Education

UNIT 2 HOST RESEARCHERS

Jim Garvin, Ph.D.
NASA Chief Scientist
NASA Headquarters, DC

Research Focus:
What can we learn from studying impact craters on Earth and Mars?

Vicky Hamilton, Ph.D.
Planetary Geologist
University of Hawai'i, HI

Research Focus:
What can Martian meteorites tell us about Mars?

Why should students learn about our solar system?

The solar system is our real neighborhood. It provides the context in which we can understand our own planet and seek answers to questions that people have long pondered. Where did we come from? Are we alone? Looking for our "roots" in the solar system, whether they be on Mars, our Moon, Saturn's moon Titan, or elsewhere, is inspiring and requires creative thinking.

What's the favorite place you've been to in your travels?

Surtsey Island off the coast of Iceland is one of my favorite places. My Maryland license plates say "SURTSEY," and people often stop to ask me what that means. I adore Iceland because of the primeval landscapes that evoke the processes we see on Mars.

When you are not working, what do you like to do for fun?

I have always been passionate about ice hockey. I played goaltender for 25 years in kid leagues, on high school, college, and club teams, and in men's leagues. I have not played much in the past few years because of the demands of my job and young children at home, but I remain a hockey fanatic. I hope to get to Mars one day and skate on its wonderful ice-caps!

What advice would you give to students who are interested in studying science?

Science is not just challenging math problems and endless homework. It's really all about exploration. You can think of the hard work involved in studying science as similar to the training athletes endure in order to participate in the Olympics or professional sports. With thought and creativity, anyone who is interested in science can find a role and participate.

What Mars-related research are you involved in currently?

One of my personal research goals is to make a connection between meteorites from Mars that are found on Earth and the source regions of those meteorites on Mars. I also analyze rocks and minerals here on Earth in an effort to better understand their properties. This improves my ability to interpret the data collected about rocks on Mars.

What do you like best about your job?

The best parts of my job are getting to look at data from another planet and being my own boss. Only a few people on Earth have seen many of the pictures and spectra that I look at every day, and that is something very exciting and special to me.

Where have you traveled for work?

On two occasions when spacecraft were launched to Mars, I went to Kennedy Space Center in Florida to watch the launches. I've helped lead field trips to sites that are geologically interesting and analogous to Mars. Some of these trips have been to Mono Lake, Death Valley, western Arizona, and Kilauea—a volcano in Hawai'i. Walking on just-cooled lava is one of the highlights of my life. For a geologist, going to a volcano and seeing lava erupt and turn into rock is a life-altering experience!

What advice would you give to students who are interested in studying science?

Know that there's a science for everyone. If you like to be outdoors and love the beach, there's a field in science that will let you be there. If you like to be indoors and work with computers, there's a field in science that will let you do that, too.

UNIT 3 HOST RESEARCHERS

Jack D. Farmer, Ph.D.
Astrobiologist
Arizona State University, AZ

Research Focus:
How does the study of extreme places on Earth help us better understand if life could exist on Mars?

Linda Jahnke
Microbiologist
NASA Ames Research Center, CA

Research Focus:
How can studying modern microbial systems help us search for signs of life on Mars?

What have you learned so far?

Mars is a complex place that differs from Earth in many fundamental ways. However, it has a history that includes water-related environments where life could have existed in the past —places that were favorable for capturing and preserving fossil biosignatures. The challenge is to find these ancient deposits! I also believe that life could still exist in the deep subsurface of Mars today.

What do you like best about your job?

The work I do is very exciting! I am a participating scientist on the NASA mission that sent the rovers Spirit and Opportunity to Mars. Getting up in the morning to explore Mars with a rover has been particularly inspiring. Each day brings new challenges and problems that require deep thought and creativity to solve. This keeps things interesting! In addition, I love working with students and enjoy the challenge of developing and communicating scientific ideas.

What was your favorite subject in school? What advice do you wish someone had given you at the time?

My favorite subjects in middle school were geology and biology. In high school, I had a great time playing football, riding in the rodeo, acting, doing improv, and playing in a rock and roll band. But I did not take my classes very seriously and, as a result, had a lot of catching up to do my first two years of college! Advice I wish I had been given? Study harder! This kind of advice was hard to come by because most of my family members never finished high school. I am the first in my family to go to college.

How did you end up in your current field?

Unlike a lot of scientists I know, I was not particularly aware of science when I was young. I loved nature and drawing, I was an awful daydreamer, and I was planning on attending an art school. My eighth-grade science class never caught my imagination. I guess I wasn't ready for it, because when I took a biology class in the summer before entering the tenth grade something happened, quite magical. I knew that I wanted to be a scientist, and a biochemist, too. I have never had any doubt since.

What do you like best about your job?

I love to learn new things. By doing research, you get to figure out new things. You're the first to know something new about how things work. I think that's great. I also love to share what I learn with my colleagues...and anyone else who will listen to me.

What one thing would you most like students to learn from participating in the *Mysteries of Earth and Mars* Expedition?

I hope students will understand that Earth is a very precious planet. Both Earth and Mars have evolved since their formation. We know that biology has had a major role in the transformation of Earth. Perhaps the same is true for Mars. Life may have evolved on both planets. Yet one planet is now a hospitable place we call home, and the other planet is probably a dead planet. We need to know why.

STUDENT HOSTS

Jeff Meng, student
University of Michigan, MI
JASON XII Argonaut

Mitchell Graves, student
Embry-Riddle Aeronautical
University, FL
JASON XI Argonaut

Jeff Meng was selected as a Student Argonaut for the JASON XII: Hawai'i, a Living Laboratory Expedition. *During the live broadcast, Jeff worked side by side with scientists researching the ecology, geology, and culture of the Hawaiian islands. He is now studying biomedical engineering at the University of Michigan.*

What is your favorite memory of your first JASON Expedition?

My favorite memory is our trip to the lava flows. We walked right up to the lava as it was oozing onto the surface and watched it flow into the sea. We used a special hammer-like tool to dig into the lava at the surface and basically "touched" some molten lava! Unfortunately, because the ground was so hot, the soles of some of our shoes melted!

How did that expedition affect your views on science and science as a career?

The expedition reinforced my love of science and increased my interest in possibly pursuing a career in science or a science-related field. It also gave me a chance to work with people who are passionate about their careers. I know I want to have that same satisfaction with whatever I choose to do.

What excites you most about this year's program, *Mysteries of Earth and Mars*?

I think it's awesome that this year's program is studying Mars. It would be neat to find out if life ever existed on Mars and if humans could possibly live there some day. The research areas of this year's expedition may provide fundamental answers to these questions.

What advice would you give to students participating in JASON this year?

I would tell students to have fun while learning everything they can from the JASON experience. JASON provides a unique opportunity to learn aspects of science not usually taught in school.

Mitchell Graves was selected as a Student Argonaut for the JASON XI: Going to Extremes Expedition. *During the live broadcast, Mitchell spent time at the NASA Johnson Space Center in Houston, Texas, where he worked with NASA scientists, engineers, and astronauts to study the International Space Station (ISS). He is now majoring in aerospace engineering at Embry-Riddle Aeronautical University.*

What is your favorite memory of your first JASON Expedition?

My favorite memory is of participating in broadcasts from the mockup of the ISS, where I executed emergency procedures. Working with astronaut Stan Love on the broadcasts was great.

What excites you most about this year's program, *Mysteries of Earth and Mars*?

Space exploration has been a dream of mine for as long as I can remember. Mars is our first major step in exploring the universe. I believe that humans have a natural desire to explore, and by exploring Mars, we can learn more about our own planet. I've said it before and I'll say it again: I want to be the first person on Mars!

What are your plans for the future?

I intend to get my bachelor's, master's, and doctorate degrees in aerospace engineering, with a second major in a space-related field. After college, I'll begin my career as an engineer, perhaps working for the government or a private company. I'd like to become an astronaut at some point, but if that doesn't work out, I'll have my own business specializing in space tourism and deep-space exploration.

What advice would you give to students participating in JASON this year?

My advice would be to ask plenty of questions. Asking questions is the best way to learn. Also, keep an open mind to all the new material you learn.

Katie Keller, student
Virginia Polytechnic Institute
and State University, VA
JASON X Argonaut

Katie Keller was selected as a Student Argonaut for the JASON X: Rainforests, a Wet & Wild Adventure *Expedition. During the live broadcast, Katie worked side by side with scientists studying the rainforests of Peru. She is now majoring in biological systems engineering at Virginia Tech.*

What is your favorite memory of your first JASON Expedition?

Oh, that's not a fair question! All my memories from being an Argonaut are my favorite. Even the ones which involve huge "bugs"—well, I think that all my memories include enormous insects—were great moments in my life. Every aspect of the JASON X year, from chatting with the other Argos and students around the world on Team JASON Online to the last live broadcast from the Amazon with Dr. Ballard, has left its mark on me.

How did that expedition affect your views on science as a career?

Before JASON, I hadn't seriously considered a career specifically in the sciences. I remember returning from the expedition feeling much

more passionate about conservation; I wanted to save the Amazon and all the other natural resources on Earth. I wanted to continue to educate people, not only about the Amazon, but about all other watersheds. Most of all, I wanted to remain an Argonaut forever and keep spreading the word about JASON.

What excites you most about this year's program, *Mysteries of Earth and Mars?*

Everything! I am always interested in learning new topics, so this year's expedition gives me a chance to take a look at another field of science that I haven't studied at school. I got to meet so many interesting people at NASA's Jet Propulsion Laboratory while taping the video segment with host researcher Kobie Boykins. Since I am an engineering student, it was very exciting to talk to Kobie and the other engineers and to see the design process and products for the rovers. I know that I couldn't do what they have accomplished, but on some small level I was able to understand some of the basic concepts they used to build the Mars Exploration Rovers.

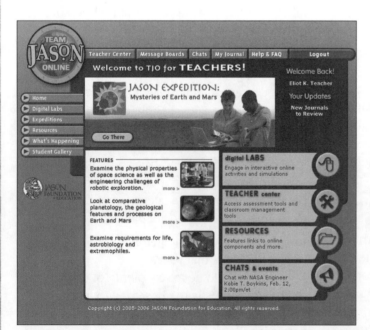

Visit Team JASON Online for more on JASON'S Host Researchers!

· **Read the full text of these interviews**

· **View a video clip of the researchers**

Go to www.jason.org, log on to Team JASON Online, and click the "Mysteries of Earth and Mars" link. Then click "Meet the Team". Not sure if you are registered on Team JASON Online? Check with your teacher.

Team JASON Online
Student Registration Instructions

Team JASON Online, or TJO, is an exciting and fun place on the Web to gain access to interactive Digital Labs, journals, and other Expedition resources for students. In addition, message boards and chat events bring you together with a worldwide community of scientists and other JASON students and teachers. Here you can share your ideas, questions, and experiences from *JASON Expedition: Mysteries of Earth and Mars*.

Team JASON Online is a protected online community that is only accessible to JASON Expedition participants. TJO gives you a fun and safe place online where you can explore science. Before you can use the resources on TJO, you need to create your own private student account.

Create a Student Account on TJO

1. Your teacher will supply you with a special Student Access Code that will allow you to begin your self-registration. Write down your Student Access Code here:

2. Go to the JASON Web site at **www.jason.org** and click the link for "Team JASON Online Login" in the upper right corner.

3. On your first visit to the Login page, you need to create a new account. Where it asks "Are you new to JASON?" select the link to "create a new TJO account."

4. Enter your First Name, Last Name, and Student Access Code in the boxes, then click "Continue."

5. Follow the instructions on screen to create a Login ID and Password. This is the information you will use each time you want to access TJO, and it will identify you as a unique user. Be sure your Login ID and Password are easy for you to remember, but hard for someone else to guess. You might want to write this information down and keep it in a safe place. For security, be sure that you don't share your ID or Password with anyone except your teacher, parents, or guardians. Once you are done creating your ID and Password, click "Continue."

6. The next screen allows you to verify your name and the Login ID that you just created. If you need to make changes, click the "Change Information" button. Otherwise click "Finish."

Congratulations, and welcome to Team JASON Online! You've just created your own student user account, and you can begin using many parts of TJO immediately. If you have a home computer with Internet access, you can log on and keep up with TJO from home. You might even want to visit TJO with your parents or guardians to share many of the exciting things that you are seeing and doing with *JASON Expedition: Mysteries of Earth and Mars*. Once your teacher fully activates the account you just created, you'll have access to the entire range of student resources on TJO.

Happy exploring!

Letter to Parents

JASON EXPEDITION:
Mysteries of Earth and Mars

Dear Parents/Guardians:

Welcome to the JASON Community!

You are invited to join your son or daughter in the remarkable *JASON Expedition: Mysteries of Earth and Mars* to explore big questions facing scientists today about the nature and history of both planets. What was the environment like on early Earth and Mars? Could there be life on Mars? How are these planets alike and different?

In this JASON Expedition, students and teachers will have a unique and exciting opportunity to:

- Explore the principles of space travel with NASA engineers who helped design the latest generation of Mars rovers and orbiters.

- Compare and contrast the geology of Earth and Mars alongside NASA's Chief Scientist and other planetary geologists.

- Accompany leading astrobiologists as they search for extreme life forms at Mars analogs — locations on Earth where environmental conditions resemble those on Mars.

Explore with us, and encourage your child by showing an interest in his or her work throughout this extraordinary educational program. Take part in any activities that the school has to offer in connection with the JASON Expedition. You can also visit JASON on the Web at **www.jason.org** to learn more about the JASON Foundation for Education and our programs.

JASON began as the dream of Dr. Robert Ballard, the scientist and oceanographer who discovered the wreck of the *Titanic* in 1986. Dr. Ballard believed that using technology to connect students and teachers in the classroom to real researchers in the field was a powerful concept. Since 1989, the annual JASON Expedition has grown into a premier, real-time science teaching and learning program for middle-grade students. JASON is proven to enhance learning outcomes for these students, based on national education standards for science, math, social studies, language arts, and technology. In addition, expedition content is correlated to all states' standards in each of these areas.

The vision of the JASON Foundation is to "Inspire in students a lifelong passion to pursue learning in science and mathematics through technology, exploration, and discovery." Past JASON expeditions have taken millions of students on exciting and educational journeys to remote research sites all over the world, including the Mediterranean Sea, the Galapagos Islands, Peru, Belize, Panama, Alaska, Hawai'i, and NASA's International Space Station, to name a few.

The new *JASON Expedition: Mysteries of Earth and Mars* is our next step in that journey of exploration and discovery, and we're very glad to have you and your child along!

©2006 JASON Foundation for Education

This picture captured by the rover Spirit in March 2004 shows the rover's view of its own tracks. Spirit's landing site was within Gusev Crater, which stretches across 165 km (103 mi). When it took this picture, Spirit was traversing a relatively smooth plain about halfway between its landing site and the rim of the much smaller Bonneville Crater, which lies within Gusev. The large rocks seen here were ejected from Bonneville by the force of the impact that formed the crater. (See MER1 location on the Map of Mars, p. 11.)

Physical Science

> ❝ These rovers are like children to the people who worked on them. They're metal and electrons and all that good stuff, but to a lot of us, these are beings who are giving us a window into what Mars is today. ❞
>
> —Kobie Boykins
> JASON host researcher

Tracy D. Drain
Systems Engineer
NASA Jet Propulsion Laboratory, CA

Research Focus:
How do the many systems of the Mars Reconnaissance Orbiter work smoothly together?

Kobie T. Boykins
Senior Mechanical Engineer
NASA Jet Propulsion Laboratory, CA

Research Focus:
How do engineers build robotic rovers to meet the grueling conditions of Mars?

Unit Contents

INTRODUCTION

In this section, you will learn about the science behind a spacecraft launch, and the challenges that NASA scientists and engineers must overcome to send a spacecraft to Mars. Then you will build and launch your own rockets to observe Newton's Laws of Motion in action.

SCIENTIST SPOTLIGHT   Tracy Drain

The Mars Reconnaissance Orbiter will use lots of energy during its mission. In this section, you will learn about forms of energy and how JASON host researcher Tracy Drain helped plan for the orbiter's energy needs. Then you will explore how scientists use friction to slow a spacecraft and guide it into a circular orbit.

SCIENTIST SPOTLIGHT   Kobie Boykins

JASON host researcher Kobie Boykins helped build the rovers Spirit and Opportunity. In this section, you will learn about the many factors that engineers must consider in designing a rover. Then you will tackle a design challenge of your own: planning, building, and testing a model spacecraft for landing a rover on Mars.

LOCAL CONNECTION

In this section, you will learn why there is currently no liquid water on the Martian surface. Then you will compare the properties of freshwater and salt water. Your challenge is to explain which type of liquid water could have existed on Mars under the widest range of environmental conditions.

SHOW WHAT YOU KNOW

You are competing in a seltzer rocket challenge. Your job is to plan modifications to a seltzer rocket so that it successfully carries a payload to a specified height.

Destination Mars

BIG QUESTION

What is the science behind a spacecraft launch

?

Focus Questions

1. What kinds of missions are sent to Mars?

2. How does NASA choose when to launch a spacecraft to Mars?

3. What is the science behind a spacecraft launch?

4. What are the challenges to sending astronauts to Mars?

Have you ever tried to sink a basketball shot from half court? If so, then you know how hard it is to hit a target from a distance. You have to aim the ball just right and throw it with just the right force and arc. But do you want a real challenge? Try shooting a spacecraft at a planet that is more than 55 million km (34 million mi) from Earth and hurtling through space at 86,000 km/hr (53,000 mi/hr). That's the challenge facing NASA when it sends a mission to Mars.

JASON host researchers Tracy Drain and Kobie Boykins helped design and build the latest generation of Mars spacecraft. Getting these spacecraft to Mars isn't simply a matter of pointing a rocket at the planet and firing. It requires the best technology, careful calculations, and a thorough understanding of the laws of physical science. In this article, you'll learn more about the challenges that NASA scientists and engineers must overcome to send a spacecraft to Mars.

The Mars Global Surveyor has orbited Mars since 1997.

1 What kinds of missions are sent to Mars?

Since 1964, NASA has sent nearly a dozen successful missions to Mars. All of these have been robotic, unmanned missions. Several other robotic missions are planned for the coming years. The table on the next page describes the four main types of Mars missions: flyby, orbiter, lander, and rover. Each mission to the planet provides important data and images, which help us understand Mars' geology, climate, and potential for supporting life.

2 How does NASA choose when to launch a spacecraft to Mars?

Earth and Mars follow different paths in their orbits around the Sun. An **orbit** is a circular or elliptical path around a planet or star. Earth and Mars circle the Sun like runners on a track: Earth on the inside lane and slower-moving Mars on the outside. Much of the time, the two planets are far from each

The Phoenix mission will send a lander to Mars in 2007.

The Four Types of Mars Missions

Mission Type	How It Works	Advantages and Disadvantages	Examples (launch date)
Flyby	The spacecraft flies by Mars without going into orbit around it. Instruments on board collect data and images, which are sent back to Earth.	During a flyby mission, a spacecraft can study multiple planets. However, scientists have only one opportunity to study each planet as the spacecraft flies by.	Mariner 4 (1964) Mariner 6 and 7 (1969)
Orbiter	The spacecraft enters into orbit around Mars and becomes an artificial satellite, circling the planet.	Orbiter missions enable scientists to study a larger portion of Mars' surface over a longer period of time. The Mars Global Surveyor, for example, has orbited Mars since 1997.	Mars Odyssey (2001) Mars Reconnaissance Orbiter (2005)
Lander	The spacecraft lands on the surface of Mars and uses its instruments to gather data and images from the planet's surface.	The lander can take actual samples from Mars' surface and atmosphere. However, landers cannot move around on the planet's surface, so they can take samples from only one location.	Viking 1 and 2 (1975) Phoenix (2007)
Rover	The spacecraft lands on Mars and is then able to travel around on the surface, gathering samples, data, and images.	Like a lander, a rover can study samples from the planet's surface. But a rover has an advantage in that it can collect data from many locations.	Spirit and Opportunity (2003) Mars Science Laboratory (2009)

other—as much as 400 million km (250 million mi) apart. Every two years, however, Earth laps Mars and the two planets pass relatively close to each other for a brief period.

You might think that the best way to get a spacecraft to Mars would be to shoot the craft straight at Mars at the moment when Earth and Mars pass closest together. This would be a good plan if Earth and Mars were not moving around the Sun. In fact, the most fuel-efficient path for a Mars-bound spacecraft is a curved path, as shown in the illustration. When the spacecraft takes off, it heads toward an empty point in space. Mars isn't there yet, but it will be when the spacecraft arrives. NASA engineers must carefully calculate the correct moment for launch. Usually, the launch occurs a few months before Earth and Mars pass closest together.

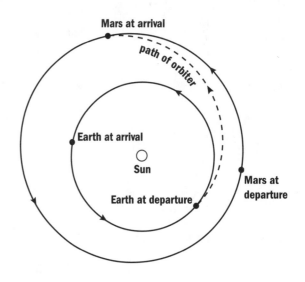

The best path for an orbiter or other spacecraft to travel from Earth to Mars is a curved path.

ARTICLE 1.1

The launch for the Mars Climate Orbiter mission shows the tremendous amount of energy needed to get a rocket into space.

③ What is the science behind a spacecraft launch?

Have you ever seen the bursts of flame and the clouds of smoke that come out of a rocket during launch? If so, you know that it takes a powerful force to lift a heavy spacecraft off its launch pad. Scientists define a **force** as a push or a pull. During a space-craft launch, there are several competing forces at work. The English physicist and mathematician Sir Isaac Newton developed a series of laws that describe these forces.

The Law of Gravity

Drop any object—a ball, a book, a hat—and it will fall to the ground. Why? Because of gravity. **Gravity** is the force of attraction between any two objects. The strength of the gravitational force depends in part on an object's mass, a measure of how much matter the object contains. The greater an object's mass, the greater the force it exerts on other objects. Our planet, Earth, is an especially massive object. Because of this, Earth exerts a powerful force on all objects on or near its surface. Earth's gravitational pull keeps you from floating off into space. It also causes dropped objects to fall to the ground.

When a rocket sits on a launch pad, it is subjected to a constant force due to gravity. The force of gravity pulls the rocket toward the center of Earth, but because Earth's surface is in the way, the rocket doesn't move. Earth's surface resists the downward force of the rocket and keeps it still.

Newton's First Law of Motion

Newton's First Law of Motion states that an object at rest tends to stay at rest, and an object in motion tends to stay in motion, unless acted upon by an outside force. What does this mean for a rocket sitting motionless on a launch pad? It means that some additional force will have to be applied if the rocket is to lift off the launch pad and overcome the force of gravity. The rocket's engines can supply this force.

Newton's Second Law of Motion

Newton's Second Law can be expressed as an equation: Force = mass x acceleration, or $F = ma$. Engineers can use this equation to calculate the force needed to launch a rocket away from Earth.

Martian
MYSTERY

Does Mars always appear to be the same brightness to human observers on Earth?

©2006 JASON Foundation for Education

To calculate force, engineers need to know:

- *The rocket's mass.* Several things contribute to a rocket's mass, including the mass of its fuel and its payload.

- *How much the rocket will need to* **accelerate** *(ak SELL uh rate), or change velocity over time.* Rockets need to reach a minimum velocity of 11,200 m/s (36,700 ft/s) to overcome Earth's gravitational pull and escape into space.

If engineers know these two variables—mass and acceleration—they can calculate the force that the rocket's engines must provide. What makes this calculation tricky is that the mass of a rocket changes during flight. As the engines fire and fuel is burned, the rocket's mass decreases. The left and right sides of the equation $F = ma$ must be equal. So, the acceleration of the rocket has to increase as its mass decreases. That is why a rocket starts off moving slowly and goes faster and faster as it climbs into space.

Newton's Third Law of Motion

Newton's Third Law explains that forces act in pairs. The law states that for every action, there is always an equal and opposite reaction. During a launch, the burning of rocket fuel produces exhaust gases that are pushed out of the bottom of the rocket. According to Newton's Third Law, there is an equal force that pushes in the opposite direction. The rocket pushes on the exhaust gases, and the gases push on the rocket. It is that force that lifts the craft into the air.

4 **What are the challenges to sending astronauts to Mars?**

NASA has not yet sent humans to Mars. However, you may see humans land on Mars in your lifetime. Someday, you might even be part of the team working on the first manned mission to Mars!

There are several challenges to sending astronauts to Mars. One is the distance. The trip to Mars could take as much as six months. The return trip could take another six months. Imagine

A skater standing on ice will move backwards after throwing a heavy ball. Newton's Third Law of Motion says that the ball will exert a force on the person, just as the person exerts a force to throw the ball.

You can learn more about the science of space travel by visiting the *Destination Mars* Digital Lab on Team JASON Online at **www.jason.org**.

Want to learn more about the latest in Mars exploration? Go to **www.jason.org/ mars_links** and check out the links for Unit 1.

how hard it would be to spend six months at a time enclosed in a small spacecraft! Astronauts traveling to Mars would most likely suffer mental and physical stress. Once on Mars, astronauts could have to wait one and a half years before traveling back to Earth. That's how long it would take for the two planets to align and provide the astronauts with the most fuel-efficient trip home. So, a round trip to Mars could take about two and a half years. In contrast, the first manned mission to Earth's moon (the Apollo 11 mission of 1969) took less than two weeks!

On Mars, astronauts would have to protect themselves from the extreme conditions of the Martian surface. Temperatures on Mars average -63 °C (-81 °F) and drop even lower at night. Mars' low atmospheric pressure could cause an astronaut's blood to boil if he or she was not enclosed in a spacesuit or landing craft. But the biggest threat would come from **cosmic radiation**, high-energy particles that are emitted by the Sun and other objects in space. On Earth, humans are protected from this type of radiation by our planet's atmosphere. Mars' thin atmosphere provides no such protection. The doses of cosmic radiation on Mars can be 1,000 times more intense than those on Earth. Astronauts would face the risk of disease if not adequately protected.

Another challenge is the great amount of fuel required to bring an astronaut home from Mars. The required fuel might even have to be produced on Mars! Rovers and landers can be left on the surface of Mars after their missions have been completed. But a human mission to Mars would not be considered a success unless the humans returned safely to Earth.

Apollo 11 astronaut Buzz Aldrin stands facing the U.S. flag on the Moon in 1969. The Moon is the only celestial body visited by humans.

Take Off!

BIG
QUESTION

**What is the
science behind
a spacecraft
launch**

?

Student Objectives

In this activity you will:

- build and launch two rockets.
- investigate whether a rocket's mass affects how high the rocket will travel.
- explain how a rocket launch demonstrates Newton's Laws of Motion.

Materials

For each student
- safety goggles

For each pair
- Activity Master 1.1A
- two film canisters
- different types of paper (copy paper, construction paper, index cards, etc.)
- scissors
- tape
- markers, crayons, or paints

In Article 1.1, you learned how Newton's Laws of Motion apply to a rocket launch. In this activity, you will launch your own rockets and observe these laws in action. First, you and your partner will build two rockets of different masses. Next, you will launch the rockets using water and seltzer tablets and measure how high the rockets fly. Finally, you will combine your data with data from your classmates and look for patterns. Does a rocket's mass affect how high it will fly? Here's your chance to find out: get ready for takeoff!

Procedure

Part 1: Build Your Rockets

1. Examine Master 1.1A. It provides instructions on how to assemble a rocket out of a film canister, paper, and tape. You will build two rockets, one of greater mass than the other. To vary the rockets' mass, you can make one rocket larger by enlarging its pieces (the tube of paper, the fins, and the cone). You can also use different types of paper for each rocket. Be creative.

2. Use scissors to cut out the paper pieces for both of your rockets. Then assemble your rockets with tape, following the instructions. Make sure that no paper or tape extends around the mouth of the film canisters, and that the canisters seal tightly when the lid is attached.

3. Decorate your rockets using markers, crayons, or paints.

4. Measure the mass of each rocket (including the film canister and lid) using the balance provided by your teacher. Enter the mass in Table 1.1A. Measure the mass in grams (g).

Part 2: Launch Your Rockets

1. Select one member of your team to measure how high the rockets fly during launch. This person should observe the rockets' flight in reference to the meter sticks against the wall.

2. Put on your safety goggles. You should wear your goggles whenever launches are taking place.

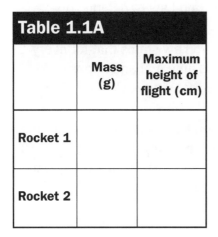

Table 1.1A		
	Mass (g)	**Maximum height of flight (cm)**
Rocket 1		
Rocket 2		

3. When it is your team's turn to launch, your teacher will provide you with a graduated cylinder, a container of water, and one seltzer tablet broken into equal halves.

4. Your teacher will hold one of your rockets upside down and remove the cap from the film canister. Put half a seltzer tablet into the canister and then add 15 mL water, using the graduated cylinder. Your teacher will quickly cap the film canister and place the rocket on the launch pad.

5. Move away from the launch pad. Then carefully watch the rocket and make observations as it launches. Be sure to observe what happens to the film canister.

6. Enter the maximum height of flight, measured in centimeters (cm), in Table 1.1A.

7. Repeat steps 4–6 for the second rocket.

Part 3: Graph the Data

1. Make a table that contains your data and your classmates' data for mass and maximum height of flight.

2. Set up a scatter plot of mass vs. maximum height of flight. Place mass on the x-axis. Examine the range of data to choose an appropriate scale for the x-axis. Place maximum height of flight on the y-axis and choose an appropriate scale. Label each axis and give the plot a title.

3. Plot each data point on the graph.

Part 4: More Launches

1. Choose one of your rockets.

2. Observe what happens to the maximum height of flight when you use a whole seltzer tablet. Compare this maximum height of flight with the same rocket's flight using a half tablet from Part 2.

3. Observe what happens to the maximum height of flight when you use a half seltzer tablet that has been crushed into powder. Compare this maximum height of flight with the same rocket's flight using a solid (uncrushed) half tablet from Part 2.

4. Observe what happens to the maximum height of flight when you use 25 mL water. Compare this maximum height of flight with the same rocket's flight using 15 mL water from Part 2.

Observations

1. During which launch did the rocket go the highest?

2. What factors seemed to affect the maximum height of flight?

3. Did the lid pop off the canister immediately after you put the seltzer tablet and water in the canister? Describe what you observed.

Conclusions

1. Did your scatter plot show any relationship between mass and maximum height of flight? If yes, describe the relationship.

2. How did your rocket launches demonstrate Newton's First Law of Motion? This law states that an object at rest tends to stay at rest, and an object in motion tends to stay in motion, unless acted upon by an outside force.

3. Newton's Second Law explains that the more massive a rocket, the more force required to launch it. But suppose you launched two rockets—one heavy, one light—using the *same* amount of force. Which rocket would you expect to fly higher? Use your results from Part 2 or Newton's Second Law to defend your answer.

4. Newton's Third Law states that for every action there is an equal and opposite reaction. How did your rocket launches demonstrate this law?

5. What have you learned to help answer the Big Question? In your JASON Journal, draft a final statement that explains the science behind a spacecraft launch.

©2006 JASON Foundation for Education

Rocket Assembly Instructions

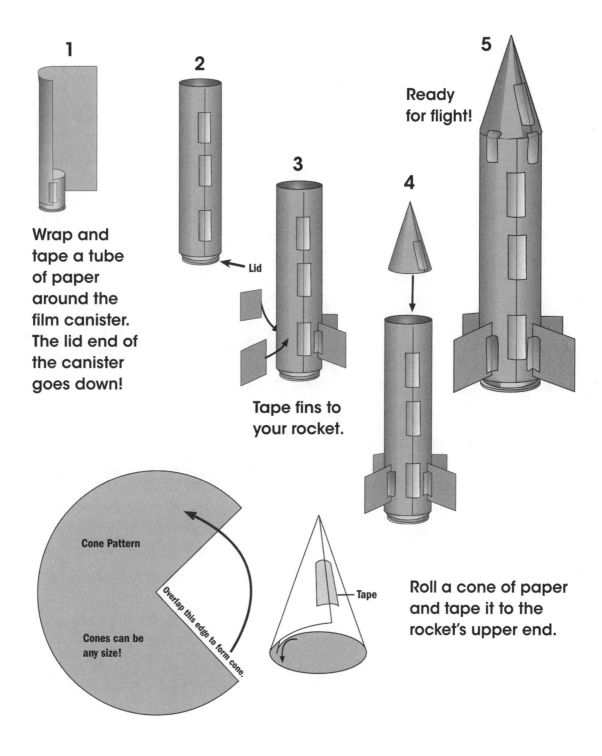

1 Wrap and tape a tube of paper around the film canister. The lid end of the canister goes down!

2 Lid

3 Tape fins to your rocket.

4

5 Ready for flight!

Cone Pattern

Overlap this edge to form cone.

Cones can be any size!

Tape

Roll a cone of paper and tape it to the rocket's upper end.

From the NASA publication *Rockets: An Educator's Guide with Activities in Science, Mathematics, and Technology*, EG-2003-01-108-HQ

ACTIVITY MASTER 1.1A

The rover Opportunity captured this view of the inner wall of Endurance Crater in November 2004. The image shows a formation called Burns Cliff. The walls of Endurance Crater have slopes that range from 18 to 20 degrees. *(See MER2 location on the Map of Mars, p. 11.)*

Energizing an Orbiter

BIG QUESTION

What are some ways that energy changes forms

?

Focus Questions

1 What is energy?

2 What are some ways that energy changes forms?

3 What forms of energy does a Mars orbiter use?

JASON host researcher Tracy Drain is crazy about energy. Drain is an engineer for the Mars Reconnaissance Orbiter, a mission with a launch date of August 2005. During its five-year mission, the orbiter will travel millions of kilometers through space. It will circle Mars thousands of times. It will operate nearly a dozen science and engineering instruments and send billions of pieces of data back to Earth. To accomplish any of this work, the orbiter needs energy. Planning for the orbiter's energy needs is a big task—one that has taken every ounce of energy that Tracy Drain and her fellow engineers have to offer!

Energy Content of Common Foods

Food	Calories
Apple	59
Chicken noodle soup (1 cup)	75
Lowfat yogurt (8 oz)	145
Ice cream bar	180
Hamburger (4-oz patty)	420

Energy Requirements for Physical Activity

Activity	Calories Burned per Hour
Walking (3 mi/hr)	320
Bicycling (12 mi/hr)	410
Swimming (50 yd/min)	500
Jogging (5.5 mi/hr)	740
Basketball	800

1 What is energy?

Energy is the ability to do work. Energy can take many forms, such as motion, light, heat, sound, and electricity. It takes energy to walk up the stairs. It takes energy to heat a house. It also takes energy to launch a spacecraft and to keep its instruments working.

There are two main types of energy: kinetic energy and potential energy. **Kinetic energy** is the energy of motion. A basketball flying through the air and a car traveling along a street both have kinetic energy. **Potential energy** is stored energy. A rubber band stretched tightly between your fingers has potential energy. Let it go and it will fly through the air.

Potential energy can be stored in different forms. A rock on a ledge has *gravitational* potential energy due to the force of gravity acting on it. The higher off the ground an object is, the greater its gravitational potential energy. Gasoline and other fuels have *chemical* potential energy. When they are burned, the energy they release can be used to do work.

Food also contains chemical potential energy. The food you eat provides the energy needed for your daily activities. The energy in food is measured in a unit called a calorie. Different activities—walking, bicycling, jogging—require different amounts of energy.

ARTICLE 1.2

② What are some ways that energy changes forms?

Energy can change from one form to another. If you push a rock off a ledge, its gravitational potential energy will change to kinetic energy as it falls. Stored energy will become energy of motion. Light a firecracker, and its chemical potential energy will turn into heat, light, motion, and sound. The change of energy from one form to another is called **energy transfer**.

Energy never disappears or gets used up. It just changes forms. When an orbiter is launched, it is a passenger on a chemically fueled rocket. At liftoff, the rocket burns a huge amount of fuel very quickly. Most of the fuel's chemical potential energy is converted into kinetic energy as the rocket gains speed to lift off the ground. Some chemical energy, however, is transferred into the shaking of the launch pad, the heat and bright light, and the roar of the rocket.

The Mars Reconnaissance Orbiter's wing-like solar panels capture energy from the Sun and convert it to electrical energy.

③ What forms of energy does a Mars orbiter use?

Thanks to its launch rocket, an orbiter leaves Earth's atmosphere and enters space at 40,000 km/hr (25,000 mi/hr). The rocket, which separates from the orbiter soon after launch, gives the orbiter all the kinetic energy it will need to travel the distance to Mars.

The Mars Reconnaissance Orbiter carries two other sources of energy: a tank of chemical fuel and a set of solar panels. As the orbiter approaches Mars and enters into orbit, some of the chemical fuel will be used by small on-board rockets to slow the orbiter and adjust its flight path. The orbiter's solar panels, which look like wings, are used to gather energy to power its science instruments and communications equipment. The panels do this using **solar energy**, energy from the Sun.

When you step into a patch of sunlight, you can feel some of the Sun's energy as warmth on your skin. The orbiter's solar panels can capture energy from sunlight and convert it into electrical energy. As the orbiter circles Mars, the solar panels rotate to stay in sunlight as much as possible. One of Tracy Drain's jobs was to make sure that the solar panels could rotate without banging into the orbiter's antenna. As long as the solar panels are working, the orbiter will never run out of energy!

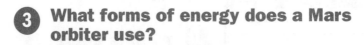

Fun Fact

During each orbit around Mars, the orbiter will experience a "day" and a "night." When Mars is between the Sun and the spacecraft, the Sun's light will be blocked and it will be nighttime for the orbiter. Without sunlight, the solar panels cannot provide energy, but the orbiter never shuts down. There are batteries on board that get recharged every "day" and supply the energy at "night."

©2006 JASON Foundation for Education

The Facts of Friction

What are some ways that energy changes forms ?

Student Objectives

In this activity, you will:

- **learn about aerobraking.**
- **observe how friction affects an object's velocity.**
- **design your own investigation of aerobraking.**

Materials

For each student
- Activity Master 1.2A

For each group
- lab stand
- clamp
- full sheet of foam core board
- small square piece of foam core board (7 cm x 7 cm)
- small rock or other object, roughly 25–50 g in mass
- masking tape
- sandpaper
- meter stick
- scissors
- glue stick

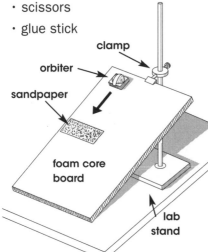

Diagram of lab setup.

What do you feel when you rub your hands together? Go ahead and try it! Do you feel some resistance as the surfaces of your palms drag against each other? If you rub fast and hard enough, you should also feel your palms get warmer. That warmth is caused by **friction**, a force that resists the motion between two surfaces in contact. Friction is at work all around us. A bike rider who drags her feet on the surface of the road is using friction to slow herself. As a result of friction, kinetic energy—the energy of motion—is converted into heat, another form of energy.

NASA uses friction in some clever ways when sending orbiters to Mars. In this activity, you will simulate how friction between an orbiter and Mars' atmosphere is used to slow the spacecraft and guide it into orbit. Get ready to learn about the facts of friction!

Procedure

Part 1: Learn the Basics of Aerobraking

1. Aerobraking is a method of slowing an orbiting spacecraft through the use of friction. Read Master 1.2A to learn the basics of aerobraking.

Part 2: Observe Effects of Friction on Orbiter Motion

1. Attach the clamp to the lab stand at a height of 50 cm. Clamp one end of the foam core board to the lab stand to form an inclined plane as shown in the diagram.

2. Tape the rock to one side of the 7 cm x 7 cm piece of foam core board. Do not let any tape wrap over to the other side of the board. The sliding side of the small board must remain flat and smooth. This weighted board represents your Mars orbiter.

3. Hold the orbiter at the top of the inclined plane, smooth-side down. Release the orbiter and observe how it moves down the incline. Repeat several times to become familiar with how the orbiter slides down the incline.

4. Use the scissors to cut a 20 cm x 10 cm strip of sandpaper.

5. On the back (smooth side) of the sandpaper strip, apply glue along both of the long edges.

6. Attach the sandpaper, rough-side up, across the left side of the foam core board, about halfway down from the top. Press it down firmly. The sandpaper needs to be as flat against the board as possible. Allow the glue to dry.

7. Place your orbiter at the top left of the inclined plane so that it will go over the sandpaper strip when it slides. Release the orbiter. Observe how the orbiter moves down the incline. Repeat several times. Write your observations in your JASON Journal.

8. Let the orbiter slide down the side of the incline that does not have the sandpaper. Then let it slide down the side of the incline that does have the sandpaper. Record any observed differences in your JASON Journal.

Part 3: Design an Investigation to Explore Aerobraking

1. Design your own investigation of aerobraking. Choose one factor as your independent variable. The factor you choose should be something that you can change, such as angle of incline, width of sandpaper strip, type of sandpaper, or orbiter mass. Draw your setup in your JASON Journal.

2. The motion of the orbiter will be your dependent variable. Based on your observations from the trials you ran in Part 2 (with and without the 10 cm–wide strip of sandpaper), form a hypothesis about what will happen to the orbiter's motion when you vary your independent variable. Write your hypothesis in your JASON Journal.

3. Experiment by adjusting your independent variable. Try at least three runs. What effects on the motion of the orbiter do you observe? Record your results.

Observations

1. Describe the motion of the orbiter as it moved down the smooth incline.

2. In what way did the motion of the orbiter change as it moved down the incline with the sandpaper in Part 2? Is that what you expected? Explain your answer.

3. In Part 3, how did varying your independent variable affect the motion of the orbiter? Was your hypothesis supported? Explain your answer.

Conclusions

1. In your model, what did the board and the sandpaper represent?

2. Did the sandpaper have an effect on the orbiter's potential energy or its kinetic energy? Explain your answer.

3. The orbiter loses energy due to friction from the sandpaper. Where does that energy go?

4. What have you learned to help answer the Big Question? In your JASON Journal, draft a final statement describing ways in which energy changes forms.

©2006 JASON Foundation for Education

Putting on the Aerobrakes

The Mars Reconnaissance Orbiter will not be able to start its scientific mission when it first enters into an orbit around Mars. That's because the orbiter's initial path around the planet will be a long, looping orbit that carries the spacecraft as close as 300 km (190 mi) to Mars and as far away as 45,000 km (28,000 mi). Such an orbit is not good for gathering data about the planet. To carry out its scientific mission, the orbiter will need to reshape its orbit so that it is traveling in a circular path around the planet, keeping a fairly constant distance from it.

Scientists have learned how to use the force of friction to adjust the spacecraft's orbit. This technique, called **aerobraking** (AIR oh BRAYK ing), allows the orbiter to conserve its limited supply of fuel. When a spacecraft aerobrakes, it dips into the upper part of Mars' atmosphere as it circles the planet. Mars' atmosphere is a mixture of gases that surrounds the planet. The passage of the orbiter through these gases creates friction, which converts some of the orbiter's kinetic energy to heat energy. By repeatedly dipping the orbiter into Mars' atmosphere, NASA is able to slow the spacecraft and bring it into the best orbit for its scientific mission.

Fun Fact

During aerobraking, the orbiter's solar panels play a special role. As the spacecraft skims through the upper layers of the Martian atmosphere, the large, flat panels act like parachutes to slow the spacecraft. The friction created as the orbiter passes through the atmosphere heats the spacecraft, especially the solar panels. The solar panels are designed to withstand temperatures of almost 200 °C (390 °F)!

NASA uses a technique called aerobraking to slow an orbiter and reshape its orbit. Each time the orbiter passes through the Martian atmosphere, it gets closer to achieving the circular orbit needed for its scientific mission.

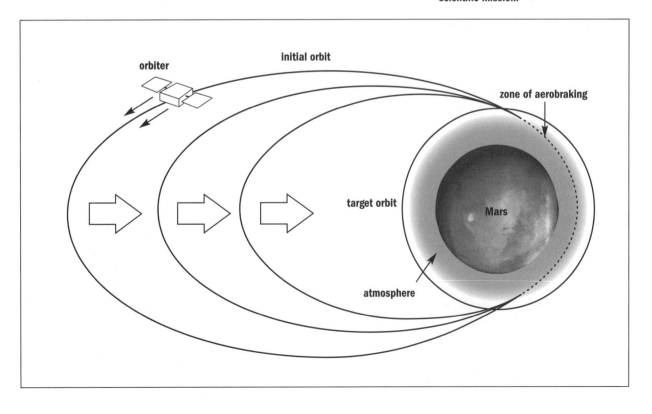

©2006 JASON Foundation for Education

This image taken by the rover Opportunity shows the southern rim of Endurance Crater and the surrounding plains of Meridiani Planum. (See *MER2 location on the Map of Mars, p. 11.*)

Building a Rover

BIG QUESTION

What are some challenges to designing rovers and landers for Mars missions

?

Focus Questions

1 What are some challenges to designing and building Mars rovers?

2 How do engineers make spacecraft lightweight, yet durable enough for space travel?

The twin rovers, Spirit and Opportunity, exceeded expectations for their exploration of Mars. This artist rendering shows what one of the rovers might look like roaming the Martian surface.

On April 30, 2004, the rover Opportunity rolled up to the rim of Endurance Crater and ground to a halt. The rover had spent the past month inching its way across a desert-like plain. Its goal? To reach this stadium-sized crater and investigate its geology. But now, with Opportunity perched at the crater's edge, rover operators at NASA's Jet Propulsion Laboratory (JPL) stopped to think. Was the path down the wall of the crater too steep? Would the rover make it to the bottom, or might it slip and fall? Once inside the crater, would Opportunity ever be able to climb back out? Was there any way of knowing?

1 What are some challenges to designing and building Mars rovers?

Knowing what a rover can and can't do is the job of JASON host researcher Kobie Boykins. A mechanical engineer at JPL, Boykins was a member of the team that designed and built the rovers Spirit and Opportunity. Boykins and his team considered many factors when designing the rovers. How much power would the rovers need? What temperatures and pressures would they experience? How small must the rovers be? Would they need to roll over large objects or up hills?

The answers to these questions helped determine the requirements that JPL had to meet in designing and constructing the rovers. For example, the JPL team knew that temperatures on

NASA created this mosaic of Endurance Crater using a number of images taken by the rover Opportunity as it was perched on the crater's rim.

ARTICLE 1.3

Fun Fact

At Meridiani Planum, the flat plain where Opportunity landed in January 2004, NASA named the craters after famous ships of exploration. Eagle Crater was named after the Apollo 11 lander that carried Neil Armstrong and Buzz Aldrin to the surface of the Moon in 1969. Endurance Crater was named for the ship that carried Ernest Shackleton's 1914 expedition to Antarctica.

Mars' surface range from -130 to 30 °C (-202 to 86 °F). Common electronic devices do not operate well over such a temperature range. Therefore, the team had to design each rover's electronic system with extreme temperatures in mind.

The team also knew that the rovers would encounter hills and sand dunes on the surface of Mars. They built the rovers to handle slopes of 35 degrees. But they also did testing and found that the chances of a rover slipping on loose soil increase on slopes greater than 20 degrees. As it happens, the walls of Endurance Crater have slopes ranging from 18 to 20 degrees. When JPL's rover operators finally made the decision to send Opportunity into the crater, they understood the risk. In the end, the risk paid off. Opportunity made it safely into the crater and emerged six months later, having made a series of exciting scientific discoveries.

2 How do engineers make spacecraft lightweight, yet durable enough for space travel?

Newton's Second Law of Motion states that the force required to accelerate an object is proportional to the object's mass. If you give a soccer ball a hard kick, you can send it flying. But kick a bowling bowl with the same force, and the ball isn't likely to move very far or very fast (plus you're going to hurt your toes!). Because of the bowling ball's greater mass, you would have to apply a lot more force to send it flying as far as the soccer ball.

Mass is an important consideration in the design of spacecraft. The more massive a spacecraft, the more force needed to launch it into space. Kobie Boykins and other engineers are constantly looking for ways to reduce mass. At the same time, they must make sure that the spacecraft they build are durable enough to withstand the extreme stresses of space flight.

One way engineers can accomplish both these objectives is by using materials called **alloys**. An alloy is a mixture of materials, usually metals. Alloys can be very different from the individual materials used to create them. Aluminum is a very light metal that is not particularly strong. Spacecraft engineers sometimes combine aluminum with other materials like zinc, chromium, and nickel. This combination of metals creates an alloy that is much stronger than plain aluminum but still very light.

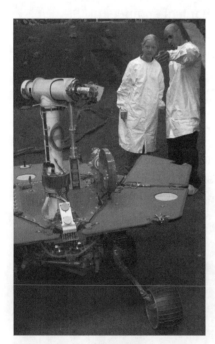

Kobie Boykins and student host Katie Keller examine a model rover at NASA's Jet Propulsion Laboratory.

Safe Landing

Student Objectives

In this activity, you will:

- **design and build a lander that meets a specific set of requirements.**
- **test your lander, evaluate its success, and identify design changes that would improve it.**

Materials

For each group

· lander building materials

· balloons	· packing peanuts
· bubble wrap	· cotton
· zip-lock bags	· tape
· cardboard	· straws
· newspaper	· toilet paper rolls
· plastic bags	· Popsicle sticks
· rubber bands	· yarn or string

· scissors

· ruler

· one raw egg (to represent the rover)

Shortly before the lander hits the surface of Mars, large airbags inflate around it, cushioning its impact. Fully inflated, the airbags stand 5.5 m (18 ft) tall.

In Article 1.3, you learned about some of the challenges that Kobie Boykins and his team face when designing a rover for a Mars mission. In this activity, you will tackle a design challenge of your own: how do you safely land a rover, with its precious cargo of instruments and equipment, on the surface of Mars? First, you will create a lander design to meet a set of requirements. Next, you will build the lander according to your design. Finally, you will determine if your lander allows you to safely land a rover from a height of 2 m (7 ft). The rover will be represented by an egg.

Some Helpful Information

The challenge of landing a rover or spacecraft on Mars is not a new one. NASA engineers have grappled with this challenge for decades, and have come up with some creative solutions. These solutions have ranged from the brilliant to the downright silly. Some of the ideas that NASA has not yet put into practice include:

- Developing a landing craft that would hover over the Martian surface and lower the rover on a tether. This is referred to as the "sky crane" method.

- Enclosing the rover in a hard honeycomb-like structure that would crush upon impact with the Martian surface. By crushing, this external shell would absorb most of the force of impact, leaving the rover undamaged inside.

- Floating the rover down to the Martian surface on a glider or inflatable balloon.

To land the rovers Spirit and Opportunity, NASA used a method that had been successful during the Mars Pathfinder mission of 1997. In this method, the rover is enclosed in a lander that is basically a protective shell. As the lander approaches the Martian surface, a parachute and rockets (mounted under the lander) are used to reduce its speed. Then, large airbags inflate around the lander, cushioning its impact as it touches down. After its initial impact, the lander bounces along the Martian surface until it rolls to a stop.

Procedure

Part 1: Design and Build Your Lander

1. Think about a design for your lander that meets the following requirements:

   a. The total mass of the lander, including the enclosed rover (egg), must not exceed 150 g (5.3 oz).

   b. Your lander can be any shape—square, round, oval, etc. However, the lander's largest dimension cannot be more than 15 cm (6 in.).

   c. You must be able to retrieve the egg from your lander without destroying the lander. You must be able to use the lander a second time.

   d. Once your lander is complete, your teacher will test it by dropping it from a height of 2 m (7 ft), over a landing target that is 50 cm x 50 cm (20 in. x 20 in.). Your lander may bounce on the ground, but it must come to a stop within the target's borders for the test to be a success.

   e. The egg must not crack or break for the landing to be a success.

2. Share ideas and create a design for your lander. Decide which materials from the list provided you will use for your lander. You may use additional materials if you have your teacher's permission. Sketch your lander in your JASON Journal.

3. Explain your group's design to your teacher before you start to build your lander. Discuss any questions or concerns with your teacher.

4. Use your design and the materials you have selected to build your lander.

5. Use the balance to determine the mass of your lander. Record the mass in your JASON Journal.

6. Use the ruler to measure the final dimensions of your lander. Record the dimensions in your JASON Journal.

Part 2: Test Your Lander and Identify Design Improvements

1. Your teacher will place a landing target on the ground. Then he or she will drop your lander to the ground from a height of 2 m (7 ft). If you wish, provide your teacher with instructions about how to do this.

2. After your lander comes to a stop, measure its distance from the landing target. Record the distance in your JASON Journal. If your lander came to a stop within the target's borders, record "on target."

3. Check the egg. If it is not cracked or broken and your lander came to a stop within the target's borders, your landing was a success. Repeat steps 1 and 2 to see if you can duplicate your success.

4. If your lander did not come to a stop within the target's borders and/or if the egg was cracked or broken, think about ways to improve your design. Discuss the design and test of your lander with your group and other class members. If there is time remaining, alter your lander design and repeat steps 1 and 2.

Observations

1. Which landers in your class were successful the first time they were dropped? What made the designs successful?

2. Which landers in your class were not successful the first time they were dropped? What made the designs unsuccessful?

Conclusions

1. Which science concepts did you apply in your design?

2. Why is it important that a lander be able to land successfully on target?

3. What have you learned to help answer the Big Question? In your JASON Journal, draft a final statement about the challenges that engineers face in designing rovers and landers for Mars missions.

What factors affect the state of water on Earth and Mars

?

Focus Questions

1. What is a phase change?

2. How does temperature affect the state of water on Earth and Mars?

3. How does atmospheric pressure affect the state of water on Earth and Mars?

Water is the only substance on Earth that exists in nature in three states: solid, liquid, and gas. You can see evidence of this fact in Earth's polar ice caps, flowing rivers, and wispy clouds. If you traveled to Mars, you would find polar caps and a few wispy clouds. But you wouldn't find any rivers. In fact, you wouldn't find any liquid water at all! Although water may have once formed lakes and carved channels on Mars, the planet is now dry. Why isn't there any liquid water on the Martian surface? Read on to find out!

1 What is a phase change?

Water cannot just disappear. It can, however, change state. The change of a substance from one state to another is called a **phase change**. When solid ice melts into liquid water, it is undergoing a phase change. When liquid water boils into the gas known as water vapor, it is undergoing a phase change. To understand why Mars is currently so dry, you must understand when and how phase changes occur.

2 How does temperature affect the state of water on Earth and Mars?

Temperature affects the state of water by influencing when a phase change occurs. To melt an ice cube, you need to heat it to a temperature of 0 °C (32 °F). This is the **melting point** of ice, the temperature at which solid water turns into liquid water. If you heat liquid water enough, it will reach its **boiling point**, the temperature at which liquid water turns into water vapor. On Earth, water usually boils at around 100 °C (212 °F). Since most places on Earth have temperatures above 0 °C and well below 100 °C, water on Earth is most often found in its liquid state.

On Mars, however, the average surface temperature is -63 °C (-81 °F). That's too cold for liquid water to exist. Most of the water on the Martian surface is frozen in the polar ice caps. Other parts of Mars are sometimes covered with a thin layer of frost.

The north polar cap of Mars is roughly 1,100 km (680 mi) across. Water remains frozen at the cap throughout the Martian year. Around the polar cap is a nearly circular dark-colored band of sand dunes.

The Viking orbiter photographed these dry channel features on the Martian surface. Scientists believe that liquid water carved the features long ago.

Martian
MYSTERY

What happened to the liquid water that used to be on Mars?

3 How does atmospheric pressure affect the state of water on Earth and Mars?

Both Earth and Mars have atmospheres. An **atmosphere** is a mixture of gases that surrounds a planet. Although invisible, an atmosphere is constantly pushing down on all objects on a planet's surface. Scientists use the term **atmospheric pressure** to describe the force on an object's surface due to the weight of the atmosphere above it.

Atmospheric pressure affects the boiling point of water. At sea level on Earth, water boils at exactly 100 °C (212 °F). Above sea level, the atmosphere gradually gets thinner and atmospheric pressure decreases. Water at the top of a 3,000-m (10,000-ft) mountain boils at 90 °C (194 °F). Because there is less air pushing down on the mountain water, it is easier for the liquid water to become a gas and escape into the air.

The Martian atmosphere is 100 times thinner than Earth's atmosphere. This thinner atmosphere results in lower atmospheric pressure. At some places on Mars, the atmospheric pressure is so low that if liquid water existed, it would boil at 0 °C (32 °F)! This temperature is also the melting point of ice. So if temperatures were to rise high enough for ice to melt, the ice would turn from a solid to a gas without ever turning into a liquid!

In the past, Mars might have had a thicker, warmer atmosphere that could have supported liquid water. Signs of ancient lakes, riverbeds, and channels suggest that liquid water did once exist on the Martian surface. But over billions of years, Mars cooled off and its atmosphere thinned. Now Mars is a cold, dry desert with only scattered signs of its watery past.

A phase diagram shows how temperature and pressure affect the state of a substance. On Earth, the atmospheric pressure at sea level is 1 atmosphere (atm). At 1 atm, ice melts at 0 °C (32 °F) and liquid water boils at 100 °C (212 °F). On Mars, the average atmospheric pressure on the surface is about 0.01 atm. At 0.01 atm, ice that reaches 0 °C (32 °F) does not pass through a liquid phase before turning into water vapor.

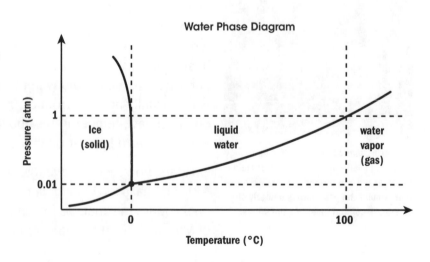

Water Phase Diagram

©2006 JASON Foundation for Education

Properties of Salt Water and Freshwater

BIG QUESTION

What factors affect the state of water on Earth and Mars

?

Student Objectives

In this activity, you will:

- **investigate some of the different properties of freshwater and salt water.**
- **explain what type of liquid water could have existed on Mars under the greatest range of environmental conditions.**

Materials

For each student

- safety goggles
- Activity Master 1.4A (optional)

For each group

- 2 petri dishes
- masking tape
- permanent marker
- 125 mL room-temperature freshwater (in container labeled *Fresh*)
- 125 mL room-temperature salt water (in container labeled *Salt*)
- medicine dropper
- 2 polystyrene cups, each filled with 200 mL crushed ice
- graduated cylinder
- plastic spoon
- thermometer (minimum range of -20 to 30 °C)
- 100 mL hot freshwater (in beaker labeled *A*)
- 100 mL hot salt water (in beaker labeled *B*)
- 60-mL clear plastic syringe

If you looked down on Earth from outer space, you would see a planet brimming with liquid water. Freshwater rivers and lakes decorate the continents. And saltwater oceans cover about 70 percent of Earth's surface.

If you looked down on Mars, you would only see signs of past liquid water. The Mars of today is too cold and has too low an atmospheric pressure to support any type of liquid water on its surface. Was the Martian climate warmer and the atmosphere thicker long ago? Probably, but nobody knows for sure what Mars' climate was like over the past few billion years. It's likely that a range of environmental conditions have existed on Mars.

In this activity, your challenge is to explain what type of water—fresh or salt—could have existed on Mars under the greatest range of environmental conditions. You will learn about some of the different properties of freshwater and salt water through a series of mini-investigations. Then you will use the results of your mini-investigations to form your explanation. Be prepared to defend your thinking!

Procedure

Part 1: Mini-Investigation: Freezing Point

1. Use the masking tape and marker to label one petri dish *A*. Label the other petri dish *B*.

2. Use the medicine dropper to squirt just enough room-temperature freshwater into petri dish *A* to cover the bottom of the dish. Squirt just enough room-temperature salt water into petri dish *B* to cover the bottom of the dish.

3. Place your two petri dishes in a freezer.

4. After 30 min, remove the petri dishes from the freezer. Record your observations about what happened to the water in each dish.

Part 2: Mini-Investigation: Melting Point

1. Label one ice-filled cup *A*. Label the other ice-filled cup *B*.
2. Use the graduated cylinder to measure 100 mL room-temperature freshwater. Pour the water into ice-filled cup *A*. Add 100 mL room-temperature salt water to ice-filled cup *B*.
3. Use a spoon to gently stir the water in each cup. Then use a thermometer to record the temperature in each cup.
4. Record the temperature in each cup every 2 min for 20 min. Be sure to gently stir the water in each cup before measuring the temperature.

Part 3: Mini-Investigation: Boiling Point at Classroom Atmospheric Pressure

1. Your teacher will boil 200 mL freshwater and 200 mL salt water.
2. Record the temperature at which each liquid boils at the atmospheric pressure in your classroom. If possible, record this atmospheric pressure using a barometer.

Part 4: Mini-Investigation: Boiling Point at Reduced Atmospheric Pressure

1. Put the pointy end of the syringe into the hot freshwater in beaker *A*. Pull up on the plunger until the syringe is about one-quarter filled with water. Keep the pointy end of the syringe underwater the whole time so that you do not pull any air into the syringe.
2. Place your thumb firmly over the tip of the syringe to seal the hole.
3. With your thumb still on the syringe tip, pull back hard on the syringe plunger until the bottom of the plunger is about 5 cm (2 in.) above the water. This reduces the pressure on the water in the syringe. Observe what happens inside the syringe.
4. Keeping your thumb on the syringe tip, slowly lower the syringe plunger. Observe what happens.
5. Record all of your observations.
6. Repeat steps 1–5 for the hot salt water in beaker *B*.

Observations

1. What happened to the freshwater when it was placed in a freezer? What happened to the salt water?
2. Describe the temperature of the ice/freshwater mixture while the ice was melting. Describe the temperature of the ice/saltwater mixture while the ice was melting.
3. Did freshwater or salt water boil at a higher temperature at the atmospheric pressure in your classroom?
4. What happened when you reduced the pressure on the hot freshwater in the syringe? What happened when you reduced the pressure on the hot salt water in the syringe?

Conclusions

1. How does salt affect the freezing point of water?
2. How does salt affect the melting point of ice?
3. How does salt affect the boiling point of water?
4. Explain whether you think liquid freshwater or liquid salt water could have existed on Mars under the greatest range of environmental conditions. Use the results of your mini-investigations to support your thinking.
5. What have you learned to help answer the Big Question? In your JASON Journal, draft a final statement about what factors affect the state of water on Earth and Mars.

©2006 JASON Foundation for Education

Data Sheet for Mini-Investigations

Part 1: Mini-Investigation: Freezing Point

Record your observations after the petri dishes are removed from the freezer.

Petri dish A (freshwater)	Petri dish B (salt water)

Part 2: Mini-Investigation: Melting Point

Record the temperature of the water in each cup every 2 min.

Minutes	Temperature in cup A (freshwater)	Temperature in cup B (salt water)

Part 3: Mini-Investigation: Boiling Point at Classroom Atmospheric Pressure

Record the temperature at which each liquid boils. If possible, use a barometer to record the atmospheric pressure in your classroom.

Boiling point of freshwater: _____

Boiling point of salt water: _____

Atmospheric pressure: _____

Part 4: Mini-Investigation: Boiling Point at Reduced Atmospheric Pressure

Record your observations about what happens when you reduce the pressure on the water in the syringe.

Freshwater	Salt water

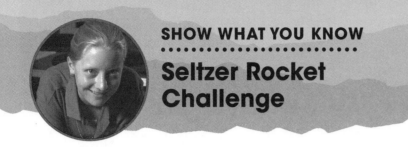

Your Name: _____ **Date:** _____

Seltzer Rocket Challenge Championship.

You are part of a team that is participating in a seltzer rocket challenge. In the first round of the competition, your team successfully launched a rocket with a mass of 15 g to a height of 200 cm. For the second round, your rocket must carry a 5-g ball of modeling clay and still reach a height of 200 cm. The clay payload must be positioned within your rocket's body tube, resting on the end of the film canister. In your role as Flight Planning Engineer, you need to determine how you will modify your first rocket to meet this challenge.

Your Challenge

Design a plan to modify your first rocket so that it will successfully carry its clay payload to a height of 200 cm. Use information from Unit 1, notes from your JASON Journal, and additional sources to prepare your plan. Your plan should:

1. Use drawings and descriptions to identify each modification that you will make to your rocket. See table below for information about the first rocket.

First Rocket	
Materials	film canister, index cards, tape
Fuel	15 mL water, ½ seltzer tablet
Height	15 cm
Width	7 cm
Mass	15 g
Payload	none

2. Explain why you selected each rocket modification and how you think each one will help your team have a successful launch. Use Newton's Second Law to help justify your modifications. If possible, use data to support your ideas.

3. List all forms of energy that will be used during the rocket's flight, and describe all energy transfers that will occur during the flight.

Conclusions

What modifications will you make to your rocket so that it will successfully carry its payload to a height of 200 cm? Why do you think these modifications will help your team have a successful launch?

Your "To Do" List: Use the table below to organize your work.

Task	Graphics (Yes/No)	Completed (Yes/No)
Identified each modification you will make to your rocket		
Explained why each rocket modification was selected, and used Newton's Second Law to help justify the modifications		
Listed forms of energy that will be used during the rocket's flight, and described energy transfers that will occur during the flight		

This picture shows the rover Spirit's view of the rolling Martian terrain at Columbia Hills within Gusev Crater. The image was taken on July 30, 2004, after Spirit had traveled more than 3 km (2 mi) from its landing site. (See *MER1 location on the Map of Mars, p. 11*.)

UNIT 2

Earth and Space Science

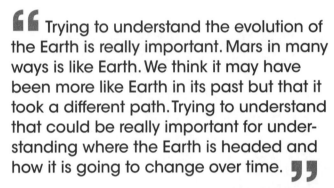

❝ Trying to understand the evolution of the Earth is really important. Mars in many ways is like Earth. We think it may have been more like Earth in its past but that it took a different path. Trying to understand that could be really important for understanding where the Earth is headed and how it is going to change over time. ❞

—Vicky Hamilton
JASON host researcher

Jim Garvin, Ph.D.
NASA Chief Scientist
NASA Headquarters, Washington, DC

Research Focus:
What can we learn from studying impact craters on Earth and Mars?

Vicky Hamilton, Ph.D.
Planetary Geologist
University of Hawai'i, HI

Research Focus:
What can Martian meteorites tell us about Mars?

Unit Contents

INTRODUCTION

In this section, you will learn how geological features and processes on Mars are similar to and different from those on Earth. Then you will analyze an image of the Martian surface to identify geological features and describe what geological processes might have formed and shaped the features.

SCIENTIST SPOTLIGHT James Garvin

JASON host researcher Jim Garvin studies impact craters—circular pits created when rocks from space smash into the ground. In this section, you will read about Garvin's explorations of impact craters on Earth and Mars. You will then have a chance to design your own investigation to explore Martian impact cratering.

SCIENTIST SPOTLIGHT Vicky Hamilton

JASON host researcher Vicky Hamilton studies Martian meteorites—rocks from Mars that have traveled through space and landed on Earth. In this section, you will learn how Hamilton studies the meteorites and what they can tell her about Mars. You will then use real data to analyze a Martian meteorite on your own.

LOCAL CONNECTION

In this section, you will learn how soil on Earth compares to soil on Mars. You will closely analyze a sample of your local soil. Then you will compare and contrast several soil samples as you try to figure out which one is the "most Martian."

SHOW WHAT YOU KNOW

A meteorite from Mars has landed on Earth. Your job is to prepare a research plan for submission to NASA that explains how you will study the meteorite. Your plan should show what you know about meteorites, impact craters, and geological processes.

UNIT 2

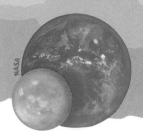

Exploring Geology on Earth and Mars

BIG QUESTION

How do scientists study Martian geology **?**

Focus Questions

1 How are the geological features on Earth and Mars similar and different?

2 How are the geological processes on Earth and Mars similar and different?

3 How do scientists study Martian geology?

Imagine that you had to design a postcard for your town. What would you choose for the picture on the front of the postcard—a building, a person, a famous landmark? Now imagine that you had to design a postcard for Mars. With no buildings or people on Mars, you might think that the front of your postcard would be boring. Think again—Mars has lots of interesting features! Mars is home to Olympus Mons (uh LIM puhs MAHNZ), the largest volcano in the solar system. And snaking along the Martian equator is Valles Marineris (VAL luhs mahr uh NEHR iss), a canyon as long as the United States. There's even a crater on Mars that looks like a smiley face!

Two people who could help you design the perfect postcard are JASON host researchers Jim Garvin and Vicky Hamilton. Garvin is Chief Scientist at NASA. One of his responsibilities is to help plan scientific missions for studying Mars. Hamilton studies **Martian meteorites**, which are rocks from Mars that have traveled through space and landed on Earth. These meteorites carry messages about the history of Mars. They are like interplanetary postcards!

Jim Garvin and Vicky Hamilton are experts in **geology**, the study of the history and structure of rocky planets. Comparing the geology of Earth to the geology of Mars is a great way to learn more about both planets.

1 How are the geological features on Earth and Mars similar and different?

Earth and Mars have many kinds of geological features in common. For example, both planets have volcanoes, mountains, canyons, polar ice caps, dunes, and craters. Some places on Earth—such as Death Valley in California or Meteor Crater in Arizona—look almost identical to certain areas on Mars.

Earth and Mars are not exactly geological twins, however. One important difference between the planets is the amount of liquid water on their surfaces. Water covers about 70 percent of Earth's surface. In contrast, there are no signs of liquid water on

Officially known as Galle Crater, this smiley face crater is located on the Argyre Planitia of Mars.

ARTICLE 2.1

the surface of Mars at present. Most of the water on Mars is frozen underground or in polar ice caps. Unlike Earth with its many oceans, lakes, and rivers, Mars appears to be very dry.

② How are the geological processes on Earth and Mars similar and different?

Scientists believe that the surfaces of Earth and Mars were once more alike. Both were probably covered with **impact craters**—circular pits that form when rocks from space smash into a planet's surface. In addition, Mars may have once had large salty lakes or oceans. What caused the differences we see today? Over billions of years, several processes changed the surfaces of the two planets. Scientists can explain many of the different geological features on Earth and Mars in terms of four processes: tectonics, volcanism, erosion, and cratering.

Tectonics

Many scientists who study geological features are interested in the crust, the outermost layer of a planet's surface. **Tectonics** (tek TAH nics) is the study of how a planet's crust moves and cracks in response to forces within a planet. Earth is said to have **plate tectonics** because its crust is made of many different plates. **Plates** are thick slabs of rock that appear to interlock like pieces of a puzzle. Earth's plates are constantly moving sideways and up and down; however, they move only a few centimeters each year. Because the plates are so massive, even small movements are very powerful. Plates grinding past each other can set off earthquakes. Plates moving apart can create cracks where lava rises into the crust. And plates smashing into each other can even make mountains. Because Earth's plates are always moving, the surface of our planet is always changing.

Tectonics on Mars is very different from tectonics on Earth. Scientists believe that the Martian crust is made of a single thick plate. When heat from the planet's interior rises to the surface, it can cause the crust to bulge and crack. Tectonics has not changed the Martian surface as much as it has Earth's surface, however, because the single Mars plate stays in one place.

One important difference between tectonics on Earth and tectonics on Mars relates to canyon formation. A **canyon** is a deep, narrow valley with steep sides. On Earth, canyons are usually cut by rivers or formed from large sideways motions of Earth's plates. The canyons we see on Mars were probably formed long ago by several processes working together.

You can learn more about geological processes by visiting the *Earth Systems* Digital Lab on Team JASON Online at **www.jason.org**. Not sure if you're registered on Team JASON Online? Check with your teacher.

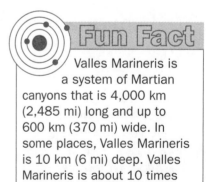

Fun Fact

Valles Marineris is a system of Martian canyons that is 4,000 km (2,485 mi) long and up to 600 km (370 mi) wide. In some places, Valles Marineris is 10 km (6 mi) deep. Valles Marineris is about 10 times longer, up to 30 times wider, and up to six times deeper than Earth's Grand Canyon!

ARTICLE 2.1

A typical Martian canyon was formed in an area with a lot of volcanic activity. Over millions of years, lava piled up and created a volcanic mound thousands of kilometers across. The weight of the giant mound pushed down on the Martian crust and formed narrow cracks. When heat from the planet's interior rose under these cracks, it caused the crust to bulge. This bulging sometimes widened a crack enough to create a canyon. Scientists believe that Valles Marineris was likely formed in this way.

Martian Canyon Formation

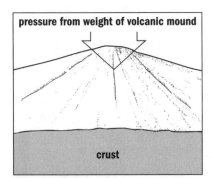

The weight of a huge volcanic mound pushed down and created narrow cracks.

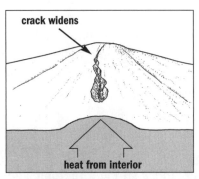

Heat from the interior of Mars caused the crust to bulge, widening one of the cracks.

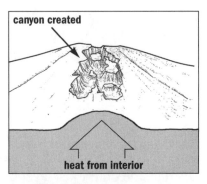

The bulging crust further widened the crack and formed a canyon.

Volcanism

Volcanism, the geological process related to volcanoes, is also important on Earth and Mars. **Volcanoes** are openings in a planet's crust through which gases, lava, and hot ashes erupt, or burst out. On Earth, volcano formation is closely related to plate tectonics. In fact, more than 95 percent of Earth's volcanoes lie along the borders of its tectonic plates. **Molten rock**, which is rock so hot that it is in liquid form, easily rises to the surface at these natural gaps in Earth's crust. Other volcanoes located away from the borders of tectonic plates form when molten rock underneath a plate pushes through to the surface. The volcanoes of Hawai'i formed in this way.

Many volcanoes on Mars look similar to the volcanoes of Hawai'i. They formed when molten rock pushed up through the Martian crust. On Earth, this type of volcano is usually tall and wide but not very steep. The volcanoes on Mars are typically not very steep either. However, some of them are much taller than any volcano or mountain on Earth. Olympus Mons, the largest Martian volcano, is nearly three times taller than the tallest volcano on Earth!

©2006 JASON Foundation for Education

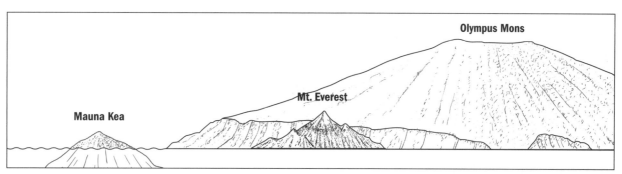

Note: Vertical scale exaggerated.

Measured from the seafloor, Mauna Kea volcano of Hawai'i is 9.7 km (6.0 mi) high. Mt. Everest—Earth's tallest mountain as measured from sea level—is 8.8 km (5.5 mi) high. Mars' Olympus Mons, the biggest volcano in the solar system, is 27 km (17 mi) high.

Although volcanoes on Mars do not seem to be currently active, lava from past eruptions covers large parts of the Martian surface. When a volcano on Mars erupted, lava oozed out like thick, hot toothpaste and built a mound that grew bigger and bigger. The lava eventually hardened and covered the surface around the volcano.

Erosion

Have you ever built a sandcastle on the beach and watched the tide come in and wash it away? If so, you have seen erosion in action. **Erosion** is the wearing down and carrying away of land by natural forces. Wind and water are two causes of erosion on Earth and Mars.

Wind on Earth wears down land and moves small particles of rock and soil from one place to another. Over time, wind erosion can change a landscape. Wind erosion is a serious problem in dry areas and along coasts where wind can easily blow away soil and sand.

Erosion in Bryce Canyon National Park created this uniquely shaped rock formation.

Wind erosion is even more widespread on Mars. The entire planet is very dry, and there are no plants to help keep the soil in place. Persistent winds form dunes almost everywhere. Large dust storms can cover nearly all of Mars for weeks at a time.

Water is another important cause of erosion. Over long periods of time, running water can cause dramatic changes, acting like a knife cutting deep into a planet's surface. For example, the water of the Colorado River cut into Arizona's surface for millions of years and formed the Grand Canyon.

Some evidence suggests that water erosion played a role on Mars, too. Orbiters have photographed features on the planet's surface that resemble dry riverbeds and channels here on Earth. Rovers have confirmed that some of the rocks on the Martian surface were once exposed to liquid water.

These dunes were formed by high winds and dust storms on Mars.

Cratering

More than 1,000 tons of space rocks fall to Earth's surface every day. Most of these rocks are smaller than a grain of sand. But occasionally a big, fast-moving rock will fall to Earth with such force that it will explode into the ground and form an impact crater. **Cratering**—the formation of impact craters—is an important geological process on both Earth and Mars. Although impact craters are still formed on the two planets, cratering was much more frequent a few billion years ago when the solar system was still young.

On Earth, plate tectonics, erosion, and other processes have buried or worn away most signs of craters. Scientists have found only about 150 impact craters on Earth's surface. That's a small number compared to the thousands of craters visible on the surface of Mars. Because Mars is not as geologically active as Earth, more craters are preserved on its surface.

Wolfe Creek Crater, one of the best-preserved impact craters on Earth, was formed about 300,000 years ago in Western Australia. The crater has a diameter of 880 m (2,890 ft).

Martian MYSTERY

Martian meteorites are rocks that left the surface of Mars, traveled in space for several million years, and finally landed at various sites on Earth. What could have caused these rocks to leave the Martian surface in the first place?

3 How do scientists study Martian geology?

Scientists who study the geology of Mars face a big challenge. They are more than 55 million km (34 million mi) away from the subject of their research! Because scientists cannot travel to Mars themselves, they must find other ways to gather clues about how the Martian surface was formed and shaped. Jim Garvin and Vicky Hamilton use many strategies to gather and study these clues.

Jim Garvin helps plan NASA missions that send robotic orbiters, landers, and rovers to Mars to study the planet. Some instruments on the robots take pictures and make detailed measurements of the Martian surface from above. Others analyze the Martian rocks and soil from the ground. Garvin uses information from these sources to study the geology of Mars.

Vicky Hamilton also uses many strategies for her research on Martian meteorites. Rocks from Mars are made out of the same ingredients as rocks from Earth. By studying Earth's rocks, Hamilton gains a better understanding of Martian meteorites. She also analyzes data gathered by NASA's missions to Mars. Hamilton is using these data to figure out where on Mars the Martian meteorites originated.

You, too, can study the geology of Mars right here on Earth. Now that you know about the major geological features and processes on Earth and Mars, join Jim Garvin and Vicky Hamilton and investigate Martian geology for yourself!

Want to learn more about the geology of Earth and Mars? Go to **www.jason.org/ mars_links** and check out the links for Unit 2.

Which Feature Came First?

BIG
QUESTION

How do scientists study Martian geology

?

Student Objectives

In this activity, you will:

- identify geological features on Mars.

- identify the geological processes that might have shaped these features.

- determine the relative ages of neighboring geological features.

Many scientists who study Martian geology need maps and pictures of Mars to help them with their work. Fortunately, recent missions to Mars have produced spectacular three-dimensional maps and thousands of images. These maps and images provide clues about how the planet's surface was formed and shaped. In this activity, you will use one of the latest pictures from Mars to study Martian geology. First, you will identify the geological features in the picture. Next, you will try to determine what processes formed the features. Finally, you will use clues to figure out whether certain features are older or younger than other features. So grab a hand lens and get ready to explore the Martian surface!

Materials

For each student

- Activity Master 2.1A
- Activity Master 2.1B
- Activity Master 2.1C
- colored pencils
- hand lens

Procedure

Part 1: Identifying Major Geological Features

1. Study Master 2.1A to review the common geological features on Mars.

2. Choose a different color for each type of feature on Master 2.1A. Lightly shade each feature in the appropriate color. You will use Master 2.1A as a key for analyzing the geological features on Master 2.1B.

3. Examine Master 2.1B carefully. Look for evidence of any of the following features: canyons, channels, volcanoes, calderas, lava flows, impact craters, and mountains. Note that not all of these features are visible on Master 2.1B. Use a hand lens to take a closer look at the various features.

4. Lightly shade each feature you identified on Master 2.1B using the matching color from Master 2.1A.

Part 2: Describing Geological Processes

1. Write down your ideas about what might have formed each type of feature you identified in Part 1. Use what you know about tectonics, volcanism, erosion, and cratering.

2. Share your ideas with your classmates.

Part 3: Determining the Relative Ages of the Features

1. Read Master 2.1C to learn how scientists determine whether one geological feature is older or younger than another geological feature.

2. Master 2.1B is divided into four quadrants labeled A through D. For each quadrant, choose two neighboring geological features to analyze. At least one of the features must be listed on Master 2.1A. The second feature could be the surface surrounding the first feature. Choose either the Principle of Cross-Cutting Relationships or the Principle of Superposition to analyze the relative ages of the two features.

3. Make a table to record the following information for each quadrant:

   a. Description of the two features you will analyze.

   b. Name of the geological dating principle you will use to analyze the features.

   c. Statement of which feature is older and which feature is younger.

   d. Explanation of how you determined which feature is older and which feature is younger.

4. Share your analysis of each quadrant with your classmates.

Observations

1. Which geological process played the major role in shaping the top half of the Gusev Crater Area shown in Master 2.1B? Explain your answer.

2. Which geological process played the major role in shaping the bottom half of the Gusev Crater Area shown in Master 2.1B? Explain your answer.

3. Do you think the top half of the Gusev Crater Area is older or younger than the bottom half? Support your answer, using what you know about geological features, processes, and dating principles on Mars.

Conclusions

1. Can you always use the Principle of Superposition or the Principle of Cross-Cutting Relationships to tell whether one feature is older or younger than another feature? Why or why not?

2. Can the Principle of Superposition or the Principle of Cross-Cutting Relationships tell you the actual age of a feature? Why or why not?

3. What have you learned to help answer the Big Question? In your JASON Journal, draft a final explanation about how scientists study Martian geology.

©2006 JASON Foundation for Education

Common Geological Features on Mars

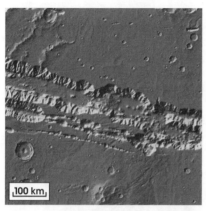

13° S, 60° W

This **canyon** has steep edges and follows a fairly straight line.

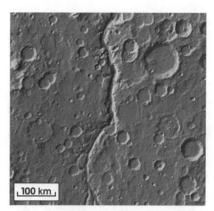

21° S, 177° E

This **channel** has smooth edges and does not follow a very straight line.

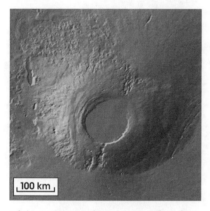

9° S, 120° W

This **volcano** has a gentle slope and smooth sides. The pit on top is a **caldera**, a volcanic crater.

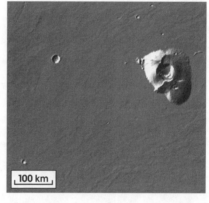

12° N, 94° W

The smooth surface and wavy lines around this volcano are typical of a **lava flow**.

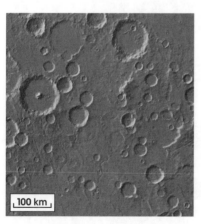

47° S, 148° W

These **impact craters** range in size from less than 1 km (0.6 mi) to almost 100 km (60 mi).

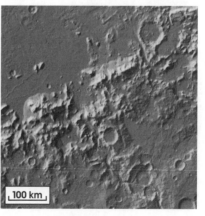

56° S, 37° W

These **mountains** have peaks that rise above the surrounding area.

Gusev Crater Area

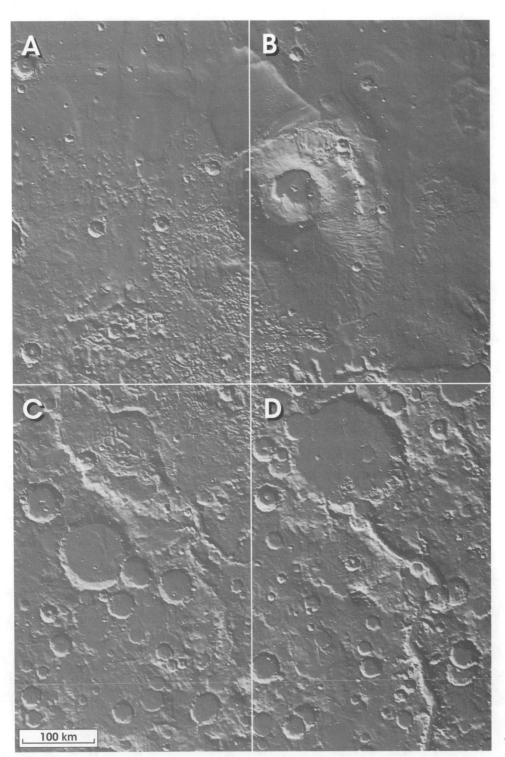

100 km

13° S, 173° E

©2006 JASON Foundation for Education

This image shows the area around Gusev Crater, where the rover Spirit landed in January 2004. Gusev is the large crater in quadrant D.

Geological Dating Principles

Scientists who study Martian geology owe a lot to planet Earth. Over the years, scientists on Earth have developed several geological dating principles. These are rules that help them figure out the relative ages of different geological features. Relative ages tell scientists how the age of one feature relates to the age of another feature. Two of these rules are the Principle of Cross-Cutting Relationships and the Principle of Superposition. By using these rules to study pictures of Mars, scientists can begin to solve the geological mystery of how the planet's surface was formed and shaped.

Principle of Cross-Cutting Relationships

This principle states that younger features cut across older features. Have you ever run your finger across a frosted cake? The mark from your finger cuts across the frosting. Anybody who looks at the cake can tell that the mark was added more recently than the frosting itself. The same thing is true on the surface of planets. A river that cuts across a rocky plain is younger than the surrounding plain. On Mars, scientists use this principle to study areas where channels, canyons, and craters have cut the surface.

This picture shows a channel feature that cuts across the surface of Mars. The Principle of Cross-Cutting Relationships tells you that the surrounding surface is older than the channel. The surface was there before the channel cut into it.

Principle of Superposition

This principle states that younger features are on top of older features. Think about a pile of clothes on the floor. The clothes on the bottom of the pile have probably been there a lot longer than the clothes on the top of the pile! On Mars, scientists use this principle to study layers of rock. They also use the principle to study areas where lava flows have filled in or buried other features.

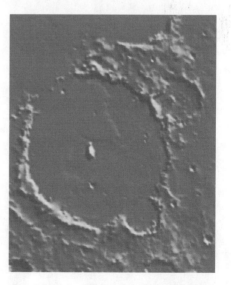

This picture shows a lava flow that spilled into a large crater. The Principle of Superposition tells you that the crater is older than the lava flow. The crater was there before the lava flowed on top of it.

ACTIVITY MASTER 2.1C

This picture taken by the Mars Global Surveyor orbiter is an aerial view of the wall of an ancient impact crater located at 42.4° S, 158.2° W in the Newton Basin in Sirenum Terra. The crater exhibits gully formations on the wall, along with patches of wintertime frost. Dark-toned sand dunes are evident on the floor of the crater. *(See location of Sirenum Terra on the Map of Mars, p. 11.)*

Making an Impact

BIG QUESTION

How do impact craters form

?

Focus Questions

1 How do impact craters form on planets?

2 How do scientists study impact craters on Earth and Mars?

3 What do scientists learn by studying impact craters?

Fun Fact

Impact craters sometimes explain important events in a planet's history. For example, scientists have linked Chicxulub (CHIK shoo loob) Crater in Mexico to a huge impact that occurred 65 million years ago. Many scientists believe that the impact led to the extinction of the dinosaurs and up to 50 percent of all living things on Earth! Chicxulub Crater is 180 km (112 mi) in diameter, and it was formed by an impactor about 10 km (6 mi) across.

JASON host researcher Jim Garvin loves just about everything related to Mars. But he has a special love for impact craters, those fascinating circular pits that dot the planet. Impact craters form when rocks from space crash into a solid planet's surface. Impact craters on Mars can be as small as a classroom in your school or as large as the state of Texas!

Because Garvin cannot travel to Mars, he needs the help of rovers and orbiters to study the craters there. Here on Earth, however, Garvin can visit impact craters himself. He has traveled to craters all over the world. He has even eaten his lunch inside a crater in Iceland!

1 How do impact craters form on planets?

Rocks from space crash into planets all the time. But most of these rocks are too small and too slow-moving to make a crater. Sometimes, however, a big, fast-moving rock will hit a planet's surface with such force that it will explode into the ground. The explosion digs a pit, forming a crater. Space rocks that create craters are called **impactors**.

The explosion produced by an impactor can release enough heat and energy to melt the entire impactor and some surrounding rocks. The explosion also sends dust and rock fragments flying in all directions. These fragments, called **ejecta**, pile up around the crater pit and form a raised **rim**. The ejecta also covers the area beyond the rim, forming what is known as an ejecta blanket. When viewed from above, the ejecta blanket looks like a ring around the crater.

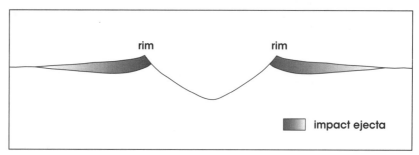

Side view of a simple impact crater.

ARTICLE 2.2

② How do scientists study impact craters on Earth and Mars?

On Earth, Jim Garvin has visited craters in places such as Arizona, Hawai'i, Germany, Iceland, and Kazakhstan (kah zahk STAN). When he visits craters, Garvin makes various measurements and studies lots of rocks. He is especially interested in unusual rocks created during an impact. Some of these rocks formed when Earth rocks melted and combined with pieces of an impactor. Garvin also studies Earth's impact craters from space. He designed an instrument that flew on the space shuttle and created three-dimensional maps of impact craters. These maps help Garvin study crater features that are hard to see from the ground.

With the help of rovers and orbiters, Garvin has studied more than 10,000 Martian impact craters. The rovers Spirit and Opportunity explored several craters and their ejecta. Both rovers took pictures, analyzed rocks, and looked for signs of past liquid water. Far above the surface, orbiters have measured the size and shape of thousands of other craters.

③ What do scientists learn by studying impact craters?

Impact craters can tell scientists a great deal about a planet. For example, impact craters can help scientists determine the age of different areas on a planet's surface. A few billion years ago, most of the Martian surface was covered with craters. However, volcanism, erosion, and other geological processes have erased signs of craters in some areas. Scientists know that these areas with very few craters are younger than other areas where many craters are still preserved.

Impact craters also uncover some of the rocks below a planet's surface. Jim Garvin likens craters to windows that let him see into the hidden parts of a planet's crust. By studying impact craters on Mars, Garvin is discovering important clues about the planet's geology. For example, some impact craters have ejecta patterns that look like dried mud. Garvin believes that these "splosh" craters are evidence of frozen water below the surface of Mars. The mud-like ejecta could have formed when the heat of impact melted underground ice and mixed it with soil and rocks. This discovery is important because water is essential to life as we know it. Impact craters may help scientists determine whether Mars was ever able to support life on its surface or underground.

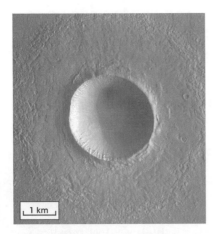

Simple impact crater on the Elysium Planitia of Mars.

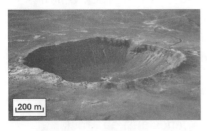

Arizona's Meteor Crater was formed 50,000 years ago when an impactor 25 m (80 ft) in diameter crashed into the desert at 65,000 km/hr (40,000 mi/hr).

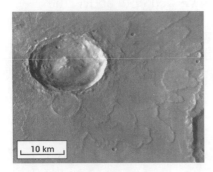

Yuty Crater, a "splosh" crater on the Chryse Planitia of Mars.

ARTICLE 2.2

Modeling Martian Craters

Student Objectives

In this activity, you will:

- explore how impact craters form.
- investigate factors that influence the size and shape of impact craters.
- create a three-dimensional model of Martian impact craters.

JASON host researcher Jim Garvin uses many strategies to study impact craters on Earth and Mars. He compares craters on the two planets using numbers, pictures, and three-dimensional (3-D) models. In this activity, you will use various strategies to study craters. First you will investigate what factors influence the size and shape of craters. Then you will create a 3-D scale model of real impact craters on the surface of Mars.

Materials

For each student

- Activity Master 2.2A
- Activity Master 2.2B
- safety goggles
- apron

For each group

- flour tray (tray filled about 5 cm deep with flour)
- large, dark-colored garbage bag
- paper cup filled with 100 mL cocoa powder or chocolate milk powder
- empty paper cup
- stick of modeling clay (¼ lb)
- 2 toothpicks
- meter stick
- metric ruler
- balance (optional)

Procedure

Part 1: Observing Crater Formation

1. Set your flour tray on top of a garbage bag.
2. Use the cup filled with cocoa powder to shake a thin layer of powder over the flour.

3. Use modeling clay to form an impactor with a diameter of about 2 cm (1 in.).
4. Drop the impactor into the flour tray from a height of about 30 cm (12 in.).
5. Use two toothpicks to gently lift the impactor from its crater.
6. Make observations of the crater using sketches, words, and numbers.

Part 2: Designing an Investigation to Explore Crater Formation

1. Brainstorm a list of different factors that might have affected the size or shape of the crater you made in Part 1.
2. Choose one factor to investigate. The factor you choose should be something that you can change, such as the diameter of the impactor or the height from which you drop the impactor. This factor will be the **independent variable** in your investigation.
3. Think about how the size or shape of a crater might change in response to changes in your independent variable. Choose a factor that you will measure each time you change your independent variable. The factor should be a measurable part of a crater, such as its diameter, the diameter of its ejecta, or its depth. This

©2006 JASON Foundation for Education

ACTIVITY 2.2

factor will be the **dependent variable** in your investigation.

4. Now write down the **research question** that will guide your investigation. Here's one possible format for your question: *How does changing [the independent variable] affect [the dependent variable]?*

5. Form a **hypothesis** that attempts to answer your research question. Your hypothesis should state *how* you think changing your independent variable will affect your dependent variable and *why* you think that.

6. List all the **controls** for your investigation. These are the factors that you will keep the same throughout the entire investigation.

7. Design at least three different experimental runs for your investigation. In each experimental run, you should change the independent variable and keep everything else the same.

8. Write a procedure for your investigation that describes each experimental run you will do and how you will record your results. Include a list of all the materials you will need for your investigation.

Part 3: Conducting an Investigation to Explore Crater Formation

1. Gather the materials you will need for your investigation.

2. Complete each experimental run in your investigation. For each run, record your measurements for the independent variable and the dependent variable.

3. Describe your results using words, pictures, tables, and/or graphs. Analyze the results to conclude whether or not your hypothesis was supported.

4. Share your findings with your class.

Part 4: Modeling Martian Impact Craters

1. In this part of the activity, you will create a 3-D scale model of the Martian impact craters shown on Master 2.2A. To begin, outline the rims of Craters A through E.

2. Measure the diameters of Craters A through E, and record this information in the table on Master 2.2B.

3. Multiply each crater diameter by the scale factor of 2 cm/1 cm to find the expected diameters for the craters in your model.

4. Using what you learned in Part 3 of this activity, develop a plan to create a 3-D scale model of Craters A through E. How large will your impactors be? From what height will you drop each one?

5. Follow your plan to create the model in your flour tray. Each crater should have the expected diameter that you calculated and the same location as shown in Master 2.2A. Creating an accurate model may involve some trial and error.

6. Complete the table on Master 2.2B by recording the final diameter of the impactor and the final drop height that you used to create each crater. Also record the actual diameter of each crater in your model.

Observations

1. What factors influenced the size and shape of the craters you made?

2. How are the craters you made similar to and different from the craters on Mars?

3. Was your first try at creating a 3-D scale model of the Martian surface successful? Why or why not?

Conclusions

1. What are some advantages and disadvantages of using 3-D models to study craters on Mars?

2. How could you make a more realistic model of craters on Mars?

3. What have you learned to help answer the Big Question? In your JASON Journal, draft a final explanation about how impact craters form.

©2006 JASON Foundation for Education

Martian Craters

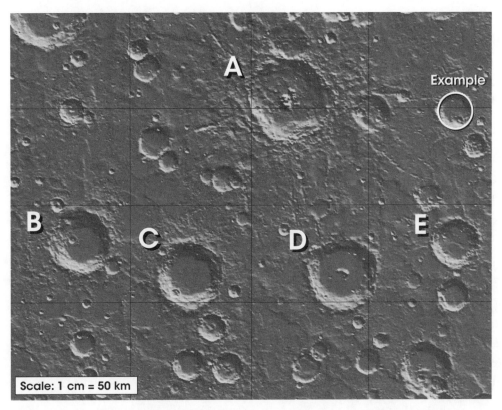

Scale: 1 cm = 50 km

These craters are located in the Oxia Palus region of Mars. Look for them on a global map of Mars at approximately 15° N, 5° W.

ACTIVITY MASTER 2.2A

Making a Model of Martian Craters

Scale Factors

A **scale factor** is a constant multiplier that converts a measurement from one size to another. Jim Garvin and other scientists use scale factors to convert distances on images of Mars to actual distances on the surface of Mars. In Master 2.2A, 1 cm on the image equals 50 km on the surface of Mars. The scale factor for the image is 50 km/1 cm (50 kilometers per centimeter). Multiply any centimeter distance on the image by this scale factor to find the actual kilometer distance on Mars. For example, you would multiply 0.9 cm—the diameter of the Example crater in the image—by 50 km/1 cm to find the actual diameter of the crater on Mars (45 km).

You will use another scale factor to change distances on the image to distances on your 3-D model. To make this easy to do, use a scale factor of 2 cm/1 cm. With this scale factor, distances on your model will be twice as long as distances on the image. For example, you would multiply 0.9 cm—the diameter of the Example crater—by 2 cm/1 cm to find the expected diameter of that crater in your model (1.8 cm).

Creating a 3-D Scale Model of Martian Impact Craters

	Crater A	Crater B	Crater C	Crater D	Crater E
Diameter of crater in image					
Model scale factor	2 cm/1 cm	2 cm/1 cm	2 cm/1 cm	2 cm/1 cm	2 cm/1 cm
Expected diameter of crater in model (Diameter in image x Model scale factor)					
Final diameter of impactor					
Final drop height of impactor					
Actual diameter of crater in model					

Investigating Mars on Earth

©2006 JASON Foundation for Education

BIG QUESTION

What can scientists learn by studying Martian meteorites **?**

Focus Questions

1 What is a Martian meteorite?

2 How do scientists study Martian meteorites?

3 What can Martian meteorites tell scientists about Mars?

One summer day in 1911, people near Nakhla (NAH klah), Egypt heard explosions and saw thick white smoke streak across the sky. Seconds later, 40 fiery rocks smashed into the ground. Scientists from many countries rushed to analyze the mysterious rocks. More than 70 years later, researchers discovered something extraordinary—the rocks were from Mars!

1 What is a Martian meteorite?

JASON host researcher Vicky Hamilton has studied these rocks. She has also studied other **Martian meteorites**, rocks from Mars that have traveled through space and landed on Earth. By comparing Martian meteorites to rocks from Earth, Hamilton learns a lot about Mars.

Rocks from anywhere in the solar system are hard, natural materials made of one or more **minerals**. Minerals are substances that have unique structures and properties. Different combinations of minerals make different kinds of rocks. Vicky Hamilton studies the mineral ingredients of Martian meteorites. She compares a meteorite's mineral recipe to data about minerals on the Martian surface. Matches help her learn more about where on Mars the meteorites might have originated.

Martian MYSTERY

How do scientists know that Martian meteorites are from Mars?

2 How do scientists study Martian meteorites?

One way scientists study meteorites is by breaking them apart. But Vicky Hamilton analyzes Martian meteorites without even touching them. She studies the radiation coming from the rocks.

Radiation is energy that travels through space in waves. Radio waves, microwaves, visible light waves, and X-rays are all examples of radiation. Different kinds of radiation have different **wavelengths.** Wavelength is the length of one wave. Vicky Hamilton focuses primarily on **infrared** (in fruh RED) **radiation**, which has wavelengths shorter than microwaves and longer than visible light waves.

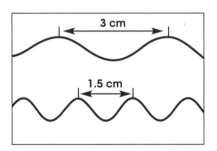

The wavelength of the top wave (3 cm) is twice as long as the wavelength of the bottom wave (1.5 cm).

ARTICLE 2.3

All objects give off infrared radiation all the time. Right now, this page, your body, and your clothes are all giving off infrared radiation! Although you cannot see infrared radiation, you can sometimes feel it as heat.

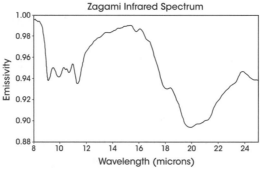

Rocks and minerals give off infrared radiation, too. Every type of mineral gives off different amounts of infrared radiation at different wavelengths. A graph of this information for any mineral looks like a squiggly line and is called a **spectrum** (plural: spectra). Each mineral has its own spectrum, which is like a fingerprint of that mineral. The spectrum of a rock such as a Martian meteorite is a combination of the spectra of all the minerals in that rock.

The Martian meteorite Zagami fell to Earth in 1962, landing about 3 m (10 ft) away from a farmer in Zagami, Nigeria. An 8-cm-wide (3-in.-wide) slice of the meteorite is pictured next to its infrared spectrum.

Vicky Hamilton uses a tool called a **spectrometer** (spek TRAH muh tuhr) to measure the infrared radiation coming from a meteorite. She graphs this information to make a spectrum of the meteorite. Then she tries to match the meteorite's spectrum to the spectra of different Earth minerals. Matches help her figure out the most likely mineral recipe for the meteorite.

3 What can Martian meteorites tell scientists about Mars?

The mineral recipe for a Martian meteorite can tell scientists a lot about how the rock formed on Mars. For example, the recipes for all Martian meteorites include minerals that were once molten, or in liquid form. This means that the rocks likely formed in volcanoes or in some other very hot place on Mars. A meteorite's mineral recipe also helps scientists to figure out if the rock was ever around water. Like rust that forms on a bike left out in the rain, some minerals form in water. If water-formed minerals are in a meteorite's recipe, the meteorite might have been exposed to water back on Mars.

Vicky Hamilton uses this spectrometer to gather data on the infrared spectra of various rocks, minerals, and Martian meteorites.

A meteorite linked to a specific place on Mars could give scientists even more information about the history of that place. Vicky Hamilton hopes to make such links. She looks for matches between the spectra of Martian meteorites and the spectra of the Martian surface. A good match could successfully link a meteorite's mineral recipe to a specific place on Mars.

©2006 JASON Foundation for Education

Martian Meteorite Mysteries

BIG QUESTION

What can scientists learn by studying Martian meteorites **?**

Student Objectives

In this activity, you will:

- graph the spectrum of a Martian meteorite.
- determine the main mineral ingredient of the meteorite.
- identify some of the possible characteristics of the area on Mars where the meteorite formed.

In this activity, you will analyze the spectrum of a Martian meteorite using a technique similar to that used by JASON host researcher Vicky Hamilton. First, you will use real data to graph the meteorite's spectrum. Next, you will compare your spectrum to the spectra of various Earth minerals. Finding the best match will tell you the main ingredient in the meteorite's recipe. Finally, you will identify some of the possible characteristics of the area on Mars where the meteorite formed. Was it dry? Was it wet? Was it hot? Was it cold? It's your mystery to solve!

Some Helpful Information

The graph of a rock's spectrum has two axes. The *x*-axis measures the different energies at which the rock radiates. Scientists often describe these energies in terms of wavelengths. Shorter wavelengths correspond to higher energies, and longer wavelengths correspond to lower energies. The wavelengths in this activity are measured in units of microns. One **micron** (MY krahn) is equal to one millionth of a meter. The width of the period at the end of this sentence is about 375 microns. An object that is only one micron wide is so small that you can't see it without a microscope!

The *y*-axis of a rock's spectrum measures how much radiation the rock gives off at each wavelength. This is called **emissivity** (ee mih SIV uh tee) and is measured on a scale of zero to one. A spectrum has peaks at wavelengths where the rock gives off a lot of radiation. A spectrum has dips at wavelengths where the rock does not give off very much radiation. You can use the number and location of these peaks and dips to compare two spectra. In this activity, you will try to identify the Earth mineral spectrum that is the best match for your Martian meteorite's spectrum. The more peaks and dips two spectra have in common, the more likely they are a match.

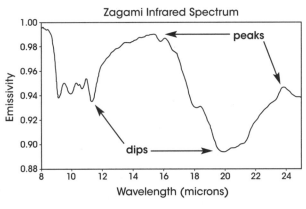

This infrared spectrum shows how much radiation the Martian meteorite Zagami gives off at different wavelengths.

ACTIVITY 2.3

Materials

For each student

- Activity Master 2.3A
- Activity Master 2.3B
- Activity Master 2.3C
- Activity Master 2.3D
- pencil
- ruler
- dark marker
- colored pencils (optional)

Procedure

Part 1: Graphing the Meteorite's Spectrum

1. Choose one of the meteorites on Master 2.3A. ALH 84001 was found in the Allan Hills region of Antarctica in 1984. Chassigny (sha sig NEE) fell to Earth near Chassigny, France in 1815. And Nakhla fell near Nakhla, Egypt in 1911.

2. Using a pencil, plot the 28 points in your meteorite's spectrum.

3. Use a pencil and a ruler to connect the points in order from left to right.

4. When your spectrum is finished, go over the pencil line with a dark marker.

Part 2: Finding the Meteorite's Main Ingredient

1. Compare the shape of your meteorite's spectrum to the shape of each Earth mineral spectrum on Masters 2.3B and 2.3C. Place a checkmark next to all Earth mineral spectra that you think might match the shape of your meteorite's spectrum.

2. To compare more closely, place Master 2.3A underneath Master 2.3B or 2.3C. Press down so that the line of your meteorite's spectrum shows through the paper on top. Line up the graph of your meteorite's spectrum with the graph of an Earth mineral spectrum to compare the location of peaks and dips.

   NOTE: You will probably not find a perfect match between your meteorite's spectrum and any single Earth mineral spectrum.

Small amounts of other mineral ingredients could add their own peaks and dips to your meteorite's spectrum.

3. Circle the Earth mineral spectrum that is most like your meteorite's spectrum. You have now identified the main ingredient in your meteorite's recipe!

4. Study the section of the table on Master 2.3D that relates to your meteorite's main ingredient. Circle any information that might help you identify possible characteristics of the area on Mars where your meteorite formed.

Observations

1. What was the easiest part about comparing your meteorite's spectrum to the Earth mineral spectra? What was the hardest part?

2. What do you think is the best Earth mineral match for your meteorite? Explain.

3. What do you think is the second-best Earth mineral match for your meteorite? How did you rule this out as the best match?

Conclusions

1. Using information from the table on Master 2.3D, can you tell if your meteorite was ever around water? Explain.

2. Is your meteorite igneous, sedimentary, or metamorphic? Does this tell you anything about whether the meteorite was formed in a hot environment or a cold environment on Mars? Explain.

3. Do you think the Earth mineral you identified is the only ingredient in your meteorite? Why or why not?

4. What have you learned to help answer the Big Question? In your JASON Journal, draft a final statement describing what scientists can learn by studying Martian meteorites.

Martian Meteorite Data

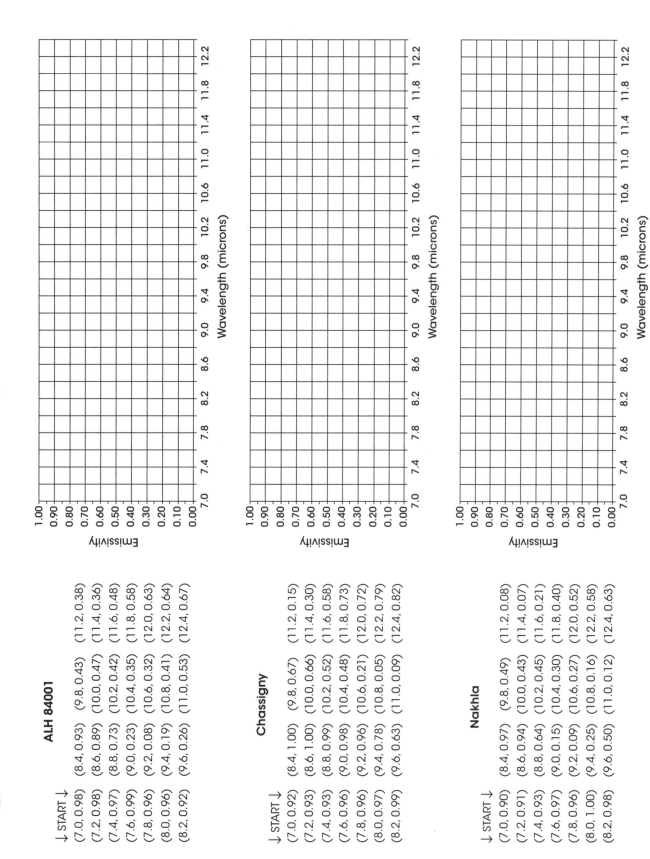

©2006 JASON Foundation for Education

ALH 84001

↓ START ↓

(7.0, 0.98)	(9.8, 0.43)
(7.2, 0.98)	(10.0, 0.47)
(7.4, 0.97)	(10.2, 0.42)
(7.6, 0.99)	(10.4, 0.35)
(7.8, 0.96)	(10.6, 0.32)
(8.0, 0.96)	(10.8, 0.41)
(8.2, 0.92)	(11.0, 0.26)
(8.4, 0.93)	(11.2, 0.38)
(8.6, 0.89)	(11.4, 0.36)
(8.8, 0.73)	(11.6, 0.48)
(9.0, 0.23)	(11.8, 0.58)
(9.2, 0.08)	(12.0, 0.63)
(9.4, 0.19)	(12.2, 0.64)
(9.6, 0.26)	(12.4, 0.67)

Chassigny

↓ START ↓

(7.0, 0.92)	(9.8, 0.67)
(7.2, 0.93)	(10.0, 0.66)
(7.4, 0.93)	(10.2, 0.52)
(7.6, 0.96)	(10.4, 0.48)
(7.8, 0.96)	(10.6, 0.21)
(8.0, 0.97)	(10.8, 0.05)
(8.2, 0.99)	(11.0, 0.09)
(8.4, 1.00)	(11.2, 0.15)
(8.6, 1.00)	(11.4, 0.30)
(8.8, 0.99)	(11.6, 0.58)
(9.0, 0.98)	(11.8, 0.73)
(9.2, 0.96)	(12.0, 0.72)
(9.4, 0.78)	(12.2, 0.79)
(9.6, 0.63)	(12.4, 0.82)

Nakhla

↓ START ↓

(7.0, 0.90)	(9.8, 0.49)
(7.2, 0.91)	(10.0, 0.43)
(7.4, 0.93)	(10.2, 0.45)
(7.6, 0.97)	(10.4, 0.30)
(7.8, 0.96)	(10.6, 0.27)
(8.0, 1.00)	(10.8, 0.16)
(8.2, 0.98)	(11.0, 0.12)
(8.4, 0.97)	(11.2, 0.08)
(8.6, 0.94)	(11.4, 0.07)
(8.8, 0.64)	(11.6, 0.21)
(9.0, 0.15)	(11.8, 0.40)
(9.2, 0.09)	(12.0, 0.52)
(9.4, 0.25)	(12.2, 0.58)
(9.6, 0.50)	(12.4, 0.63)

Earth Mineral Spectra – Part 1

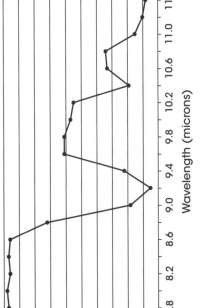

Wavelength (microns)

Emissivity

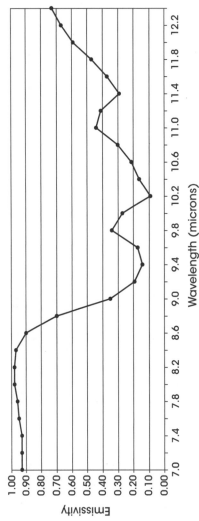

Wavelength (microns)

Emissivity

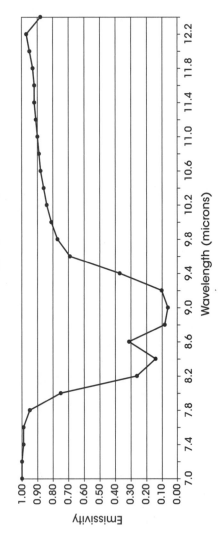

Wavelength (microns)

Emissivity

Augite
(AW jite)

Augites is the Greek word for brightness; some samples of augite are very bright.

Orthopyroxene
(or thoh py RAHK seen)

Pyro comes from the Greek word for fire; orthopy-roxene is found in volcanic rock.

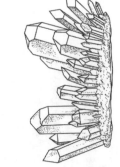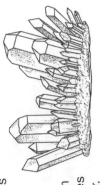

Quartz
(KWORTS)

Clear quartz has no water in it; milky quartz gets is cloudy white color from very tiny bubbles filled with water.

©2006 JASON Foundation for Education

Earth Mineral Spectra – Part 2

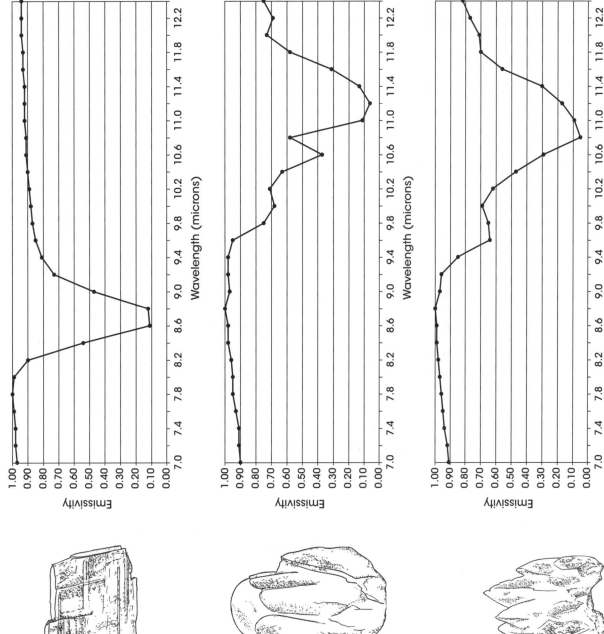

Gypsum
(JIP suhm)

Gypsum is soft enough to scratch with your fingernail.

Olivine Fo10
(AH luh veen foh 10)

High quality olivine is known as peridot (PEHR ih doh), the birthstone for August.

Olivine Fo68
(AH luh veen foh 68)

Olivine Fo68 has less iron and more magnesium than olivine Fo10, but otherwise the two types of olivine are very similar.

Earth Minerals Data Table

Earth Minerals Data

Mineral Name	Typical Color	Type of Rock in Which Mineral Is Usually Found	How Mineral Relates to Water	Streak	Hardness
augite	dark green, brown, black	igneous	turns into clay and other minerals when exposed to water	greenish white	5–6
gypsum	gray, white, colorless	sedimentary	previously dissolved in seawater; forms when the water evaporates	white	2
olivine Fo10	light green, colorless, pale yellow-green, greenish black	igneous	turns into clay and other minerals when exposed to water	white	6.5–7
olivine Fo68	light green, colorless, pale yellow-green, greenish black	igneous	turns into clay and other minerals when exposed to water	white	6.5–7
orthopyroxene	white, colorless, gray, light brown, pale green	igneous, metamorphic	turns into clay and other minerals when exposed to water	white	5–6
quartz	clear, white, purple, pink, gray	igneous, sedimentary, metamorphic	very resistant to water; not likely to turn into other minerals when exposed to water	white	7

Data Table Vocabulary

- **Igneous** rocks form from hot, melted rock material that cools and becomes solid.

- **Sedimentary** rocks form when rock or mineral fragments are compressed or cemented into solid layers.

- **Metamorphic** rocks form when high temperatures and pressures cause igneous rocks or sedimentary rocks to change form.

- **Streak** is the color of a mineral in its powdered form. This color is obtained by rubbing the mineral across a hard, rough surface and observing the mark it leaves.

- **Hardness** indicates a mineral's resistance to scratching or cutting. This is often measured by the mineral's position on the Mohs Scale of Hardness. Talc is the softest mineral, a 1 on the scale. Diamond is the hardest mineral, a 10 on the scale. A mineral can scratch any mineral lower than it on the hardness scale, but it can be scratched by any mineral higher than it. For example, your fingernail has a hardness of about 2.5, so it can scratch gypsum but not augite.

©2006 JASON Foundation for Education

Digging up the Dirt

BIG QUESTION

How does soil on Earth compare to soil on Mars

?

Focus Questions

1 How does soil on Earth compare to soil on Mars?

2 Why do scientists study soil?

Fun Fact

Soil on Earth supports a lot of life that is invisible to the naked eye. A single teaspoon of garden soil can contain over 1 billion bacteria, about 120,000 fungi, and 25,000 algae!

Martian **MYSTERY**

Why is Mars called the red planet?

What do ants, tomato plants, and baseball pitchers have in common? They all depend on **soil**, the loose covering on a rocky planet's surface. Earth's soil provides a home for ants, nutrients for plants, and a place for pitchers to stand. But soil is important for many other reasons. In fact, soil directly or indirectly supports most of the life on Earth.

Mars also has a lot of soil, although it is quite different from Earth's soil. Scientists are very interested in Martian soil because it could hold a key to the search for life. Does the soil contain evidence of past life? Could it support life now? Read on to dig up the fascinating dirt on Mars and Earth!

1 How does soil on Earth compare to soil on Mars?

Soils on both Earth and Mars contain minerals, bits of rock, and gases. But other than these basic ingredients, soils on the two planets do not have much in common. Earth's soils almost always contain water and a lot of **organic matter**, which is living or dead plant and animal material. Soils on Earth vary from place to place. Every environment has its own type of soil with its own unique combination of minerals and organisms. These variations cause differences in color. Your local soil could be brown, black, red, orange, yellow, or even green!

Scientists have not yet found liquid water on the surface of Mars. But they have found evidence suggesting that there might be both liquid and frozen water in soil beneath the surface. Scientists have also looked for organic matter in Martian soil. So far, they have not found any signs of living or dead organisms. They have found that soil on Mars seems to be fairly similar across the entire planet. This might be due to the frequent dust storms that constantly pick up the soil, mix it together, and move it from place to place. Most Martian soil is reddish-brown and looks like finely ground cinnamon. Walking on Mars would feel like walking on a rocky and very dusty dirt road.

ARTICLE 2.4

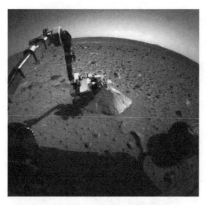

The rover Spirit used its mechanical arm to examine rocks and soil on Mars.

2 Why do scientists study soil?

Scientists study soil on Earth to learn more about how it supports life. For example, scientists study how different types of soil store water and **nutrients** (NOO tree uhnts). Nutrients are the vitamins, minerals, and other materials that all living things need to live and grow. Scientists also study soil on Earth to make sure that it is healthy. Soil is home to many organisms, including trees, flowers, mushrooms, moles, and termites. Most of the food we eat comes from plants and animals that depend on soil in some way. If soil does not have enough nutrients or if it is polluted with chemicals, many living things suffer. Scientists study how to protect soil and how to keep it clean.

Scientists study soil on Mars for different reasons. Some scientists look for signs of life in the soil. Although none of their tests have turned up life so far, they have not stopped looking. Other scientists study the soil to find out how its characteristics could help humans who might someday travel to Mars. Could the soil be used to grow healthy plants? Could it be used as a building material? Astronauts on Mars would definitely want to know the answers to these questions. They might even want to know if Martian soil would make a good pitcher's mound!

Gullies line the wall of this Martian impact crater, and sand dunes cover the crater floor. Some scientists believe that the gullies could have formed when liquid water beneath the soil was released onto the surface.

1. Beetle
2. Millipede
3. Centipede
4. Chipmunk
5. Aster
6. Ants
7. Mushrooms
8. Oak tree
9. Mole
10. Earthworm
11. Pill bug
12. Termite
13. Beetle larva
14. Moss

On Earth, soil provides a home to a wide variety of organisms.

©2006 JASON Foundation for Education

Soil Sleuthing

Student Objectives

In this activity, you will:

- analyze a local soil sample.

- compare and contrast local soil samples to Martian soil simulant.

Most people do not think about the billions of organisms living under their feet. Soil might not look alive, but almost all of the earth on Earth is packed with life. Martian soil, on the other hand, is thought to be lifeless. In this activity, you will first practice studying a local sample of soil. Then you will examine several different soil samples. All of them except one will be from places near your school. The non-local sample will be **Martian soil simulant**, which means that it will look similar to soil from Mars. Your job will be to observe all of the soil samples and determine which one is the "most Martian." Be prepared to defend your answer!

Materials

For each student

- Activity Master 2.4A
- disposable gloves (if handling soil)

For each station

- local soil sample (for Part 1)
- additional soil sample (for Part 2)
- tweezers
- 4 toothpicks
- 2–4 hand lenses
- 2–4 rulers
- 2–4 magnets (optional)
- high-powered magnifier (optional)
- other materials needed for soil tests (to be determined by class)

Procedure

Part 1: Observing a Local Soil Sample

1. Use the tools at your station to examine your soil sample. For this part of the activity, all of the samples are the same.

2. Write down observations about your sample on Master 2.4A.

3. Share your observations with your class.

4. As a class, brainstorm different ways you could observe or determine the characteristics of a soil sample.

5. As a class, choose five ways to observe or determine the characteristics of the different soil samples in Part 2 of this activity. Record these choices in the gray boxes on Master 2.4A.

Part 2: Comparing Local Soil to Martian Soil Simulant

1. Carefully observe the soil sample at each station. All of the samples except one are from places near your school. The non-local sample is Martian soil simulant. Use the guidelines your class developed to record your observations about each soil sample on Master 2.4A.

2. After you have observed all of the soil samples, write down a hypothesis about which sample you think is the Martian soil simulant.

3. Share your hypothesis and your reasoning with the rest of your class.

Observations

1. What were some of the similarities among the local soil samples?
2. What were some of the differences among the local soil samples?
3. Did you see signs of life in any of the soil samples? Use words and drawings to explain your answer.

Conclusions

1. What are some possible reasons that none of the local soil samples looked exactly alike?
2. Which soil sample did you think was the Martian soil simulant? How did you form your hypothesis? How could you test your hypothesis?
3. What have you learned to help answer the Big Question? In your JASON Journal, draft a final explanation about how soil on Earth compares to soil on Mars.

JASON host researcher Vicky Hamilton and student host Mitchell Graves closely examine the soil in Death Valley, California.

©2006 JASON Foundation for Education

Observation Table

Part 1: Observing a Local Soil Sample

Soil Characteristics					
	Color	Texture	Smell	Signs of Life	Other Observations
Local soil sample					

Part 2: Comparing Local Soil to Martian Soil Simulant

Soil Characteristics					
Sample 1					
Sample 2					
Sample 3					
Sample 4					
Sample 5					

ACTIVITY MASTER 2.4A

A Mystery Rock from Outer Space

> **" I believe that humans have a natural desire to explore, and by studying Mars we can learn more about our own planet. "**
>
> —Mitchell Graves,
> Student Host and
> Former JASON XI Argonaut

Your Name: _____ **Date:** _____

National Meteorite Research Center. Year 2019: A meteorite from Mars has landed on Earth. Many scientists would like the opportunity to study it. Analyzing the meteorite could help scientists learn more about the mineral composition of Mars and the geological processes that shaped the Martian surface. The head of the scientific laboratory where you work has asked you to prepare a research plan to study this meteorite. The proposed plan will be submitted to NASA.

Your Challenge

Prepare a research plan to study the meteorite. This plan will be presented at a meeting with NASA officials next month. Use information from Unit 2, notes from your JASON Journal, and additional sources to prepare your plan. Make sure you include the following:

1. How the meteorite from Mars arrived on Earth.
2. How you will determine the mineral composition of the meteorite.
3. How you will use the information you gather to determine how the meteorite formed.
4. How you will use information from science experts, such as Jim Garvin and Vicky Hamilton, in your study. This information should include descriptions of the tools and methods that the scientists use in their studies, the results of their research on the process of impact cratering, and the nature of meteorites.

Conclusions

What methods will you use to study the new meteorite from Mars? What questions might you be able to answer with the data you will collect?

Your "To Do" List: Use the table below to organize your work.

Task	Sources	Graphics (Yes/No)	Completed (Yes/No)
Described how the meteorite from Mars arrived on Earth			
Identified the methods that will be used to analyze the meteorite			
Explained how data will be used to determine how the meteorite formed on Mars			
Gathered and summarized data on impact cratering			
Gathered and summarized data on meteorites			

Kasei Valles is a system of very large, ancient outflow channels. This aerial image from the Mars Global Surveyor orbiter shows a portion of the youngest channel system in the Kasei Valles region. Torrents of mud, rocks, and water carved this channel, exposing layers of Martian terrain along its walls. The picture covers an area 3 km (1.9 mi) across, located near 21.1° N, 72.6° W. (See the Map of Mars on p. 11 to locate these coordinates slightly to the left of VIK1.)

Life Science

> **❝** To understand whether we are alone in the universe is one of the great intellectual challenges of our age. Life may be present in many places in the universe. But in our lifetime, Mars offers us our best chance to know. **❞**
>
> —Linda Jahnke
> JASON host researcher

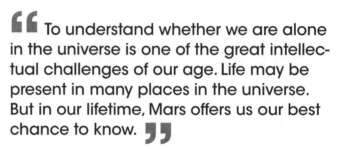

Jack D. Farmer, Ph.D.
Astrobiologist
Arizona State University, AZ

Research Focus:
How does the study of extreme places on Earth help us better understand if life could exist on Mars?

Linda Jahnke
Microbiologist
NASA Ames Research Center, CA

Research Focus:
How can studying modern microbial systems help us search for signs of life on Mars?

UNIT 3

Unit Contents

INTRODUCTION

In this section, you will learn about astrobiology—the study of life in the universe. You will find out what scientists know about the requirements for life on Earth and whether these requirements could be met on Mars. Then you will investigate which of three mystery samples exhibits characteristics of life.

SCIENTIST SPOTLIGHT Jack Farmer

JASON host researcher Jack Farmer studies extremophiles—organisms that live in extreme conditions on Earth. In this section, you will learn how Farmer's work adds to our understanding of the types of life that could survive on Mars. Then you will explore whether the microorganism yeast is an extremophile.

SCIENTIST SPOTLIGHT Linda Jahnke

JASON host researcher Linda Jahnke studies biosignatures—signs of past or present life. In this section, you will learn how Jahnke's work with biosignatures on Earth trains her to recognize what biosignatures might look like on Mars. Then you will use a technique called chromatography to further explore biosignatures.

LOCAL CONNECTION

In this section, you will learn how an ecosystem's abiotic characteristics— non-living factors such as temperature, pH, and salinity—influence the types of life that can survive there. You will conduct a field investigation at a local aquatic site. Then you will compare your data with those of Jack Farmer and Linda Jahnke.

SHOW WHAT YOU KNOW

You are invited on a manned mission to Mars to search for signs of life. Your job is to prepare a mission plan that explains where you would look and why.

UNIT 3

The Search for Life

Focus Questions

1. What is astrobiology?

2. What are the requirements for life?

3. Does Mars have the requirements for life, or did it in the past?

Have you ever looked up at the night sky and wondered whether life exists on other planets? If you have, you're not alone. Just think of all the books and movies that tell about journeys through space or visitors from other parts of the solar system.

Scientists have long looked beyond Earth in the search for life. Because Mars is Earth's neighbor and is similar to our planet in many ways, it offers an ideal place to start. JASON host researchers Jack Farmer and Linda Jahnke are both exploring the possibility of life on Mars.

1 What is astrobiology?

Astrobiology (AS troh by AHL uh jee) is the study of life in the universe. It includes the study of life's development on Earth, as well as the search for life on other planets. Studying how life developed on our planet will help us understand whether life could have developed on other planets, including Mars.

Humans' ideas about the potential for life on Mars have changed sharply over the past 100 years. Around the beginning of the 20th century, an astronomer named Percival Lowell announced that he had found evidence of life on Mars. Looking through a telescope, Lowell saw what he thought was a network of canals on Mars' surface. Lowell believed that a civilization of intelligent beings had built cities in the warmest regions of Mars, near the equator. These beings, Lowell hypothesized, had dug canals to transport water from the polar ice caps. While Lowell's theories were criticized by some scientists of his day, they nevertheless became popular. Science fiction writers expanded on his ideas, writing fantastic tales about visits to Martian cities.

But in the decades that followed, scientists found major flaws in Lowell's ideas. As bigger and better telescopes became available, scientists determined that there was no network of canals on Mars' surface. They also learned that the conditions on Mars are much harsher than Lowell had thought.

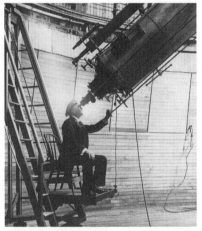

More than 100 years ago, the astronomer Percival Lowell believed he had found evidence of life on Mars.

Want to learn the latest about the search for life on Mars? Go to **www.jason.org/mars_links** and check out the links for Unit 3.

©2006 JASON Foundation for Education

In 1976, NASA landed the Viking I spacecraft on Mars—the first craft ever to land safely on the surface of another planet. The pictures sent back by Viking I put an end to any ideas about cities and intelligent life on Mars. They showed a bleak, desert-like landscape, nothing but rocks and sand in every direction. Instruments on the lander found no clear evidence of life in the Martian soil. Suddenly, it seemed the odds of finding life on Mars were almost zero.

② What are the requirements for life?

Recently, however, scientists have discovered life in some very unexpected places on Earth. These discoveries have caused people to rethink their ideas about the conditions under which life can survive. Researchers have found organisms living in Antarctic ice and deep beneath Earth's surface. They have found life in boiling hot springs and in lakes many times saltier than the ocean. Maybe it is not so far-fetched to believe that Mars might host life, too—perhaps deep underground, or within its polar ice caps. Maybe we just have to know where and how to look!

We can start by asking the question, what does life really need to survive? Scientists agree that life on Earth requires three things—liquid water, nutrients (NOO tree uhnts), and energy. They assume these things are necessary for life to exist anywhere in the universe.

Liquid water

Your body is about two-thirds liquid water, by weight. Green plants are up to 95 percent water. So it's not surprising that liquid water is the most basic requirement for life. All living cells contain liquid water. This water plays a number of key roles. It transports nutrients to and within living cells. It carries waste away from cells. And it also acts as a solvent, which means it dissolves chemical substances within organisms, assisting in body processes such as the digestion of food.

Water can only play these roles in its liquid form. Think about how your body would function if the water inside of you was a solid or a gas. How would your body digest the food you eat or carry important nutrients to your cells? Fortunately, water remains liquid over an unusually large range of temperatures— from 0 °C (32 °F) to 100 °C (212 °F). Because most places on Earth have temperatures within this range, liquid water—and life—exist in nearly every place on this planet.

The surface of Mars looks lifeless in this image from the Viking lander.

Nutrients

Nutrients are the raw materials that all living things need to live and grow. Minerals found in Earth's soil, water, and air are the most basic form of nutrient. Other, more complex nutrients are created within living organisms. For example, plants make nutrients such as sugars through the process of **photosynthesis** (foh toh SIN thuh sis). During photosynthesis, plants use sunlight as an energy source to combine water and the gas carbon dioxide. This process produces not only nutrients, but also the oxygen that many life forms breathe.

The first life forms that evolved on Earth were capable of extracting mineral nutrients directly from their environment. Today, plants and some microorganisms still extract nutrients in this way. Animals, including people, get their nutrients by eating plants and other living things.

Energy

All life requires **energy**, which is the ability to do work. On Earth, different organisms get their energy from different sources. Scientists use a model called a **food chain** to track how energy passes from one organism to another. A simple food chain that occurs in Death Valley, California, involves mesquite shrubs, the desert cottontail (a type of rabbit), and red-tailed hawks. The mesquite grows using the Sun's energy for photosynthesis. The cottontail gets energy by eating mesquite. And the hawk gets energy by eating cottontails.

Photosynthetic organisms use sunlight as an energy source to combine water and the gas carbon dioxide. This process produces oxygen and sugars (a form of nutrient).

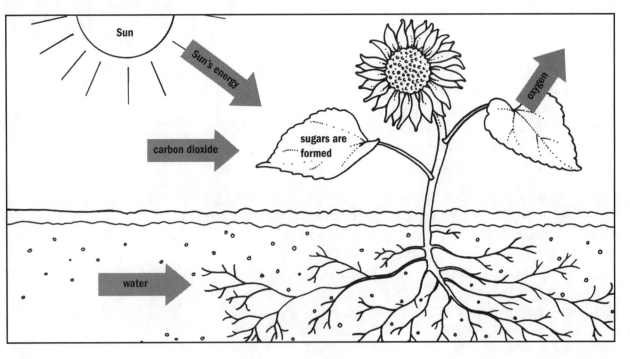

©2006 JASON Foundation for Education

ARTICLE 3.1

The Sun provides the energy that drives most food chains on Earth. Plants convert the Sun's energy into chemical energy. When other organisms eat plants, the chemical energy is passed up the food chain. But what about communities of organisms living underground or in ocean depths, where there is no sunlight? They need a different source of energy. In these environments, the base of the food chain is formed by microscopic organisms that use chemicals from beneath Earth's surface or from other processes as energy sources. Using chemicals from the environment to create the energy needed for life is called **chemosynthesis** (KEE moh SIN thuh sis).

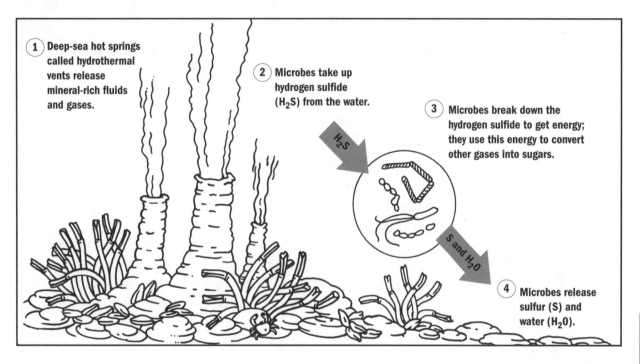

1. Deep-sea hot springs called hydrothermal vents release mineral-rich fluids and gases.

2. Microbes take up hydrogen sulfide (H_2S) from the water.

3. Microbes break down the hydrogen sulfide to get energy; they use this energy to convert other gases into sugars.

H_2S

S and H_2O

4. Microbes release sulfur (S) and water (H_2O).

3 Does Mars have the requirements for life, or did it in the past?

To determine whether life could have developed on Mars, scientists use what they know about the three requirements for life: liquid water, nutrients, and energy. If all three exist or existed on Mars, there is some chance life may have developed there.

Scientists have already found two of these things. Recent Mars missions have provided NASA scientists with detailed information about the chemistry of the planet's rocks and soils. From these data, scientists have concluded that the surface of Mars has most of the mineral nutrients necessary for life. Mars also has several possible energy sources. Its surface receives light energy from the Sun. In addition, Mars has sources of the

In the deep sea, where sunlight is unable to penetrate, microbes get the energy needed for life through a process called chemosynthesis.

ARTICLE 3.1

Martian MYSTERY

The rover Opportunity sent back images of something very strange in Mars' rocks. Scientists studying these small, round formations called them "blueberries." What were these blueberries and how did they form?

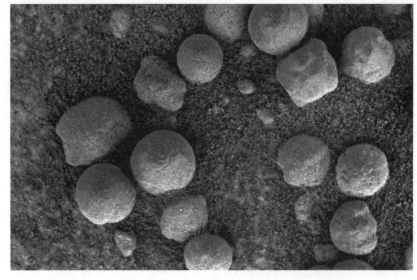

The rover Opportunity took this picture of the unusual gray formations that scientists have dubbed "blueberries." The average diameter of a blueberry is 4 mm (0.2 in.).

ADD TO YOUR Journal

Do you believe there might be life somewhere else in the universe? Why or why not? If your answer is yes, what do you think the life might look like?

chemicals needed for chemosynthesis. The only requirement for life missing on Mars' surface is liquid water.

Due to the environmental conditions on Mars, liquid water cannot exist on the planet's surface. A pan of water left on Mars' surface would turn to vapor or freeze. Recent data show that water does exist as ice at Mars' North and South Poles. Water ice also lies under large regions of the planet's surface. It's possible that liquid water could exist beneath Mars' surface, too. And if it does, organisms that use chemosynthesis could live there—a fact we know because organisms have been found living deep within Earth's crust. NASA is currently developing tools for drilling beneath the surface of Mars to look for water, and for life.

Scientists might find that Mars does not have liquid water now but did in the past. There is strong evidence that liquid water once flowed over Mars' surface. Pictures of Mars show features that look like the paths of ancient river channels. Some Martian rocks also contain minerals and salts that indicate the rocks were once covered by liquid water.

Recent findings by the rovers Spirit and Opportunity have convinced Jack Farmer and Linda Jahnke that Mars once had the ingredients for life. This has added a special urgency to their work. Farmer is studying the types of organisms that might be able to survive in Mars' harsh conditions. Jahnke is developing techniques for searching for signs of Martian life. Read on to learn more about their work!

©2006 JASON Foundation for Education

It's Alive!

©2006 JASON Foundation for Education

How do scientists search for life on Earth and beyond?

Student Objectives

In this activity, you will:

- identify some characteristics of living things.
- design tests to look for signs of life in three samples.
- use data to support your conclusion about which sample contains life.

Materials

For each student
- safety goggles
- plastic gloves
- Activity Master 3.1A

For each group
- 3 sealed plastic bags labeled A, B, and C, each filled with an unknown substance
- 2 plastic spoons
- tweezers or 2 toothpicks
- hand lens
- beaker of cold tap water
- beaker of warm water
- 3 white paper plates
- 6 clear plastic cups

How do you know if something is a living thing? Sometimes it is obvious, as when you see a bird flying or a spider weaving a web. But sometimes it is not so clear. A pail of water scooped from a pond might not look like it contains life. But a powerful microscope would reveal a world of living things in each drop. A dry desert might look lifeless. But if you visited after a spring rain, you might find that it had burst into bloom. Sometimes life is too small to see easily, and sometimes it is dormant, or inactive, for long periods of time.

Scientists looking for life on Mars struggle with this same question: Will they recognize life when they see it? To avoid mistakes, scientists use a number of tests to help them classify something as living or non-living. In this activity, you are the scientist. It is up to you to design your own tests! One of the three samples in front of you contains living things. You need to figure out which one. Use any of the materials provided and your senses of sight, smell, hearing, and touch to solve the mystery.

Procedure

1. As a class, brainstorm ways in which you might tell the difference between a living and a non-living thing. Create a list on the board of some characteristics of living things.

2. Collect your group's three substances, A, B, and C. Take a few minutes to do an initial observation of each substance, using only your unaided eyes. Make notes of any similarities and differences you see among the substances.

3. Within your group, decide on three simple tests you will perform to determine which substance contains life. As you design your tests, remember to:

- think about what things life needs in order to survive (look back at Article 3.1, if necessary).
- use your senses of touch, smell, hearing, and sight.
- refer to the list of characteristics of living things on the board for ideas.

4. Briefly describe your tests on Master 3.1A. *Hint:* Divide each substance into three equal parts, so that you can use one-third for each of your three tests.

5. Perform each test and record your observations on Master 3.1A. Be sure to record any changes to the substances. Draw pictures of what you observe.

6. As a group, decide which substance contains life. Assemble data to support your conclusion. Data can be in the form of pictures or descriptions of your observations.

Observations

1. When you first observed the substances, what similarities and differences did you find?
2. What similarities and differences among the substances did you observe during your various tests?

Conclusions

1. Which substance do you think contains life? Why?
2. How did you use what you learned about the requirements for life to help you design your tests? Explain.
3. What have you learned to help answer the Big Question? In your JASON Journal, draft a final statement that demonstrates what you now know about how scientists search for life in the universe.

Test Data Sheet

Test 1 Description:

_____

_____

Test 1			
Substance	**A**	**B**	**C**
What do you observe?			

Test 2 Description:

_____

_____

Test 2			
Substance	**A**	**B**	**C**
What do you observe?			

Test 3 Description:

_____

_____

Test 3			
Substance	**A**	**B**	**C**
What do you observe?			

ACTIVITY MASTER 3.1A

The Twin Peaks are modest-sized hills to the southwest of the Sojourner landing site. They were discovered in the first panoramic photographs taken by the rover on July 4, 1997. The peaks are approximately 30 m (100 ft) high and 1 km (0.6 mi) from where Sojourner took this picture. (See *MPF location on the Map of Mars*, p. 11.)

Life in the Extremes

How can studying extreme environments on Earth help scientists look for life on Mars?

Focus Questions

1 What are extreme environments and what lives in these environments?

2 How can studying extreme environments on Earth help scientists look for life on Mars?

J ASON host researcher Jack Farmer guides a boat past an island covered in ash. Hot springs spray jets of water from the island. Oddly shaped towers rise meters above the lake surface. Jack Farmer often describes his work as "looking for life in all the wrong places," and this research site in Mono Lake, California, certainly does look strange. The lake formed in a volcanic basin. Water flows in but cannot flow out. As the lake water evaporates, salts and minerals are left behind. As a result, the water is **alkaline**, which means it has a high pH, almost like pure detergent. It is also almost three times as salty as the ocean. Mono Lake is an extreme environment.

To find out more about extremophiles and whether life could survive on Mars, visit the *Extreme Microbes* Digital Lab on Team JASON Online at **www.jason.org**. Not sure if you're registered on Team JASON Online? Check with your teacher.

1 What are extreme environments and what lives in these environments?

Extreme environments are places where conditions are at the outer limits of the ranges in which life can survive. They include places you might think of as too hot, too cold, too dry, or too dark for life to exist. Mono Lake is an extreme environment because its waters have a very high pH and are very salty, or **hypersaline** (HY puhr SAY leen). Another of Jack Farmer's research sites, the hot springs of Yellowstone National Park, are boiling hot. Some of them are also very **acidic** (uh SIH dik), meaning they have a low pH. Other extreme environments include deserts, ice sheets, ocean floors, deep caves, and underground environments that are kilometers beneath Earth's surface.

Limestone towers give Mono Lake an alien appearance.

ARTICLE 3.2

In the 1970s, JASON chief scientist Robert Ballard and a team of scientists discovered a community of organisms living near hydrothermal vents. Hydrothermal vents are deep-sea hot springs. They form when plates in Earth's crust move apart on the ocean floor, creating an opening through which boiling water and poisonous gases rush out. The conditions near hydrothermal vents—extreme heat and acidity, total darkness, and enormous pressure—are among the most extreme on Earth. The discovery of life near these vents forever changed people's ideas about the limits of life.

Giant tubeworms live near hydrothermal vents, openings in the seafloor from which boiling water and poisonous gases rush out.

People have always been interested in exploring Earth's extreme environments. But only recently have biologists found that many of these areas are teeming with life! Organisms that thrive in extreme environments are called **extremophiles** (ik STREE muh files). What do extremophiles look like? Not like most creatures you know! Giant tubeworms rise from the deepest parts of the ocean floor. Algae turn the surface of Arctic snow red. And bacteria (single-celled organisms) live deep within Earth. The majority of life forms discovered in extreme environments are **microorganisms**, living things so small they can be seen only with a microscope. Most microorganisms are made up of a single cell, the smallest unit of life.

❷ How can studying extreme environments on Earth help scientists look for life on Mars?

Like Mono Lake, many extreme environments look absolutely alien. But when Jack Farmer uses the word "alien," he really means it! He studies how extremophiles live in Earth's extremes in order to understand how life might have developed on Mars.

Many extreme environments on Earth have conditions similar to those on Mars. Because of those similarities, scientists use Earth's extreme environments as **analogs** (AN uh logz), or real-life models. Researchers study ice sheets in Antarctica as analogs for Mars' polar regions. Deserts such as Death Valley are analogs for dry regions near Mars' equator. Earth's caves and underground environments allow scientists to observe what energy and nutrients might be available to life beneath the surface of Mars.

Some of Earth's extreme places resemble environments that might have existed on Mars in the distant past. Many scientists believe that billions of years ago, liquid water covered parts of Mars. Hypersaline lakes probably formed in some deep craters, where water could flow in but not out. Could any life form have survived in such a highly salty environment? Jack Farmer hopes to answer this question by studying the organisms that live in the salty waters at Mono Lake. These organisms have developed special adaptations that allow them to put up with the extremes of their environment. So it is not out of the question that similar organisms might once have flourished on Mars. Jack Farmer is exploring that possibility. For him, Mono Lake is a window into Mars' past.

Extreme Adaptations

©2006 JASON Foundation for Education

How can studying extreme environments on Earth help scientists look for life on Mars ?

Student Objectives

In this activity, you will:

- collect and analyze data on the responses of yeast to different environmental conditions.

- identify some environments in which yeast is active.

- draw conclusions about how studying extreme environments on Earth can help scientists look for life on Mars.

Jack Farmer studies extremophiles called **cyanobacteria** (SY uh noh bak TEER ee uh). These single-celled microorganisms can live in a variety of extreme environments. In this activity, you will explore how well another single-celled life form, yeast, fares in extreme conditions.

Your class will split into five groups. Each group will test how well yeast responds to extremes in a specific environmental condition. The five conditions that the groups will test are: acidity (low pH), alkalinity (high pH), heat, cold, and salinity. Is yeast an extremophile? It's up to you to find out!

Some Helpful Information

Your group will receive three bottles. Each bottle represents a different variation of the environmental condition you are testing. For example, if you are in the acidity group, your three bottles will represent the following conditions: high acidity, medium acidity, and neutral (no acidity). You will add sugar and yeast to all three bottles and then cap each bottle with a balloon. When yeast is active and reproducing, it releases carbon dioxide (CO_2) gas into the air. The balloons capture the carbon dioxide gas. You will measure the relative amount of gas produced under different conditions by measuring the circumference of the balloons. The more gas produced, the more active the yeast.

Materials

For each student
- Activity Master 3.2A
- Activity Master 3.2B
- graph paper
- pencil
- plastic gloves
- safety goggles

For each group
- 3 test solutions
- 6 teaspoons active dry yeast in a sealable plastic bag
- ¾ teaspoon sugar in a sealable plastic bag
- set of measuring spoons
- small funnel
- 3 balloons (9 in. or smaller)
- clock or stopwatch
- several meters of string
- scissors
- metric ruler

Procedure

1. Collect your group's three test-solution bottles from your teacher.

2. Use the funnel and measuring spoons to pour ¼ teaspoon of sugar into each bottle. The sugar provides the yeast with nutrients.

3. Add 2 teaspoons of yeast to each bottle.

4. Quickly cap the mouth of each bottle with a balloon. Then swirl the yeast, sugar, and

a) Add sugar and yeast to each bottle.

b) Cap each bottle with a balloon.

c) Measure each balloon's circumference.

liquid solutions gently. Set the bottles down on a flat surface.

5. After 5 min, measure the circumference of each balloon. To measure circumference, wrap a piece of string around the balloon's thickest part. Then cut the string and measure its length in cm using the ruler. Record the measurement in the appropriate column on Master 3.2A. If your balloon does not inflate, record a 0.

6. Measure the balloons every 5 min for 30 min or until the balloons stop getting larger. Record all measurements on Master 3.2A.

7. Prepare a line graph for each balloon. Put time elapsed (5 min, 10 min, etc.) on the horizontal axis (*x*-axis). Put the circumference measurements (in cm) on the vertical axis (*y*-axis). Plot and label the data for all three balloons on the same graph.

8. Prepare a bar graph, with test variations (for example, pH) on the *x*-axis and circumference measurements (in cm) on the *y*-axis. Graph and label the final circumference measurement for each variation of your environmental condition.

9. Present your group's data to the class. Look at all of the data together to determine the ranges of temperature, salinity, and pH in which yeast are most active.

10. As a class, debate whether yeast can be considered an extremophile. Read Master 3.2B to learn about some of the extreme conditions that other organisms have adapted to.

Observations

1. Which, if any, of your group's balloons inflated? Specify for which variation(s) of your environmental condition the balloon(s) inflated.

2. Which balloon inflated at the fastest rate?

3. Which balloon ended up with the largest circumference?

Conclusions

1. Which variation of your environmental condition was best for yeast activity? Explain your answer.

2. Do you think yeast thrives in extreme environments? Why or why not?

3. What have you learned to help answer the Big Question? In your JASON Journal, summarize what you now know about how studying extreme environments can help in the search for life on Mars.

Extreme Adaptations Data Sheet

Balloon Circumference (in cm)			
Time	Test Solution 1	Test Solution 2	Test Solution 3
5 min			
10 min			
15 min			
20 min			
25 min			
30 min			

Record-Holding Extremophiles

Now *That's* Extreme! Record-Holding Extremophiles		
Category	**Extreme Condition**	**Record Holder**
Hottest	121 °C (250 °F)	Microorganisms in underground well at Lidy Hot Springs, Idaho
Coldest	-15 °C (5 °F)	Lichen, a combination of fungus and algae, living in Antarctica
Deepest	3.2 km (2 mi) underground	Bacteria living between rock grains in Earth's crust
Most acidic	pH < 0	Bacteria in caves
Most basic	pH 13	Bacteria in evaporative lakes, such as Mono Lake
Longest in space	6 years in space	Bacteria in a NASA satellite
Saltiest	300 parts per thousand (ppt)	Bacteria in hypersaline lakes, such as Guerrero Negro, Mexico
Highest pressure	1,200 times standard atmospheric pressure	Bacteria at the bottom of the Marianas Trench, the deepest point in the ocean

Signs of Life

BIG QUESTION

How does the study of biosignatures help scientists search for life on Mars

?

Focus Questions

1. What is a biosignature?

2. How does the study of biosignatures help scientists search for life on Mars?

Have you ever seen footprints in the mud or found a bird's nest in the crook of a tree? Perhaps you were lucky enough to find a shell on a beach or the imprint of a snail preserved in rock. What you saw—footprints, a nest, a shell, a fossil—were signs of life that had been left behind.

JASON host researcher Linda Jahnke specializes in looking for signs of life. But the signs she looks for cannot be seen with the unaided eye. Jahnke is a **microbiologist**, someone who studies life that can be seen only through a microscope. And the signs she looks for, the biosignatures of microorganisms, are often microscopic as well.

1 What is a biosignature?

A **biosignature** is a sign of present or past life. **Fossils**, the traces or remains of living organisms from a past geologic age, are the most familiar biosignatures. Some fossils are the actual body parts of organisms, preserved in rock. Many museums, for example, display fossils of shells or dinosaur bones. Fossils can also record the movements or behaviors of living things. Examples of this type include fossilized tracks, burrows, and even tooth marks in rock!

A fossilized shell. Fossils are the most familiar biosignatures.

Fossils are not the only biosignatures, however. Scientists can also detect living things by the chemicals they leave behind in the environment. Every type of living thing, from the largest animal to the tiniest microorganism, is made up of a unique blend of chemicals. After death, living things break down into their chemical parts. By analyzing traces of chemicals in Earth's rocks and soils, scientists can sometimes figure out what lived in a particular location.

Linda Jahnke and student host Jeff Meng examine a microbial mat sample in the NASA Ames greenhouse.

Martian MYSTERY

In 1984, scientists found a Martian meteorite in an ice field of Antarctica. After examining this potato-sized meteorite with high-powered microscopes, some scientists concluded that certain formations in the rock are the tiny fossils of microorganisms. Are these formations actual evidence of life on Mars?

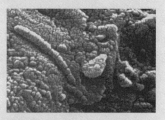

This tube-like formation is less than 1/100th the width of a human hair.

Want to peek inside Linda Jahnke's greenhouse at NASA Ames? Then go to **www.jason.org/ mars_links** and click on the link to the *Greenhouse One* Web site. The site features a remotely operated Webcam that gives you a live look inside the greenhouse and lets you zoom in on Jahnke's microbial mats.

Chemicals in the air can be biosignatures, too. For example, oxygen gas is produced by green plants and certain microorganisms during photosynthesis. Before the first photosynthetic life developed on ancient Earth, the atmosphere contained very little oxygen. Today, however, oxygen is plentiful. The abundance of oxygen in Earth's atmosphere can be seen as a sign that our world is filled with photosynthetic life. Mars' atmosphere, on the other hand, contains very little oxygen.

❷ How does the study of biosignatures help scientists search for life on Mars?

Scientists searching for evidence of life on Mars face a challenge: How will they recognize the signs of life when they see them? By studying biosignatures here on Earth, scientists can train themselves to recognize the signs that Martian life might leave behind.

That is what Linda Jahnke does. She studies the biosignatures of **microbial mats**. Microbial mats are thick, spongy formations made of layers of microorganisms. Scientists believe that microbial mats were among the first life forms to arise on Earth, more than 3 billion years ago. Scientists also believe that microbial mats might once have lived on Mars, in the extreme conditions of ancient lakes or oceans.

The microbial mats that Linda Jahnke studies exist in some extreme environments on Earth, such as the salty ponds of Guerrero Negro (geh REHR oh NAY groh), Mexico. Samples of these mats have been transported to the NASA Ames Research Center in California. There, in an unusual greenhouse, Jahnke and fellow researchers grow and analyze the living mats. They also develop methods that will help them look for the chemical biosignatures of ancient microbial mats on Earth and Mars.

Through her research, Linda Jahnke has discovered that modern microbial mats are similar to those that existed billions of years ago on Earth. How does she know? Chemical biosignatures! Jahnke compared chemical biosignatures in modern mats with those in fossilized mats in ancient rock. She found they were the same. Maybe someday she will have the chance to compare Earth's microbial mats with mats from Mars!

ARTICLE 3.3

ACTIVITY 3.3

Get the Signature!

BIG QUESTION

How does the study of biosignatures help scientists search for life on Mars ?

Student Objectives

In this activity, you will:

- **use a method called chromatography to analyze the chemical biosignatures of life forms.**

- **compare chemical biosignatures from different life forms.**

- **draw conclusions about how the study of biosignatures on Earth helps scientists search for signs of life on Mars.**

Materials

For each student

- Activity Master 3.3A
- Activity Master 3.3B
- safety goggles
- plastic gloves

For each group

- 2 filter paper strips (4 cm x 11 cm) mounted on Popsicle sticks
- 2 clear 16-oz plastic cups (at least 12 cm high)
- 2 toothpicks
- petri dish containing 5 mL crushed spinach
- petri dish containing 5 mL crushed carrot
- 90 mL isopropyl alcohol
- small sheet of wax paper (about 20 cm x 20 cm)
- white paper plate
- metric ruler
- colored pencils (yellow, orange, pink, red, blue, and green)

JASON host researcher Linda Jahnke believes that microbial mats might once have existed on Mars, at a time when that planet was likely covered by salty lakes or oceans. If so, the mats may have left chemical traces in Mars' rocks and soils. The question is, what specific chemicals might the mats have left behind?

To answer this question, Linda Jahnke studies the chemical makeup of microbial mats on Earth. One method she uses is called **chromatography** (kro muh TAH gruh fee). In chromatography, a chemical mixture is passed through a material that separates it into its chemical parts. This leaves a unique chemical signature. In this activity, you will use a simple technique, called paper chromatography, to separate the chemicals in two common vegetables. Then you will compare the biosignatures you obtain with a biosignature from one of Linda Jahnke's microbial mat samples.

Procedure

Part 1: Chemical Biosignature of a Microbial Mat

1. Read Master 3.3A to learn more about how paper chromatography works.

2. On Master 3.3B, look at the diagram of the chromatogram labeled "Microbial Mat." It shows the outlines of colored bands formed when Linda Jahnke performed chromatography on a sample of her microbial mat. Each band represents a different pigment.

This cross section of a microbial mat shows many layers of different organisms.

©2006 JASON Foundation for Education

ACTIVITY 3.3

3. Using colored pencils, color in the bands according to the pigment key at the bottom of the master. The numbers within the bands correspond to the pigment colors listed in the key.

Part 2: Chemical Biosignatures of Spinach and Carrot

1. In your group, you will perform paper chromatography on two vegetables: spinach and carrot. Your teacher will provide your group with two filter paper strips that have been taped onto Popsicle sticks. Each paper strip should have a pencil line 2 cm (0.8 in.) from the bottom.

2. Dip a toothpick into the crushed spinach and use it to paint a green line over the pencil line on one of the strips. Allow the strip to dry and then paint a second green line over the first. Try to get as much spinach color on the line as possible.

3. Dip a second toothpick into the crushed carrot. Use it to paint a thin, orange line over the pencil line on the second paper strip. Let the strip dry and then repeat this step to get as much carrot color on the line as possible.

4. Carefully pour half of the isopropyl alcohol into the bottom of each of the two clear plastic cups.

5. Lay each Popsicle stick across the rim of a cup, as shown on Master 3.3A. The paper strips should hang down into the cups, and the bottom edge of each strip should be submerged about 1 cm (0.4 in.) deep in the alcohol.

6. Wait 15 min, or until the alcohol travels most of the way up the strips.

7. Remove the paper strips from the alcohol. Lay them on wax paper to dry for a few minutes. Then place the dry strips on a white paper plate.

8. Observe the bands of color on the paper strips. Each color represents a different pigment that is present in the spinach or carrot. The patterns formed by these colored bands are your chromatograms, or chemical biosignatures, for spinach and carrot.

9. Using colored pencils and a ruler, draw pictures of your chromatograms for spinach and carrot on Master 3.3B. Use the key on the master to determine the names of the pigments in each chromatogram.

10. Compare your chromatograms for spinach and carrot with others in the class. Then compare them with the microbial mat chromatogram.

Observations

1. For each of the chromatograms (spinach, carrot, and microbial mat), how many pigments did you find? What are the names of the pigments?

2. How did your spinach and carrot chromatograms compare to those of your classmates?

3. How did your chromatograms compare to the chromatogram of the microbial mat?

Conclusions

1. What kind of information can chromatography provide?

2. If scientists found what they thought were fossils of microbial mats on Mars, how might they use chromatography to support this idea?

3. What have you learned to help answer the Big Question? In your JASON Journal, draft a final explanation about how studying biosignatures can help scientists look for life on Mars.

How Paper Chromatography Works

Linda Jahnke uses a sophisticated form of chromatography to separate the chemicals in microbial mats. But for this activity, she examined the chemical makeup of a mat using a simpler technique, called paper chromatography. This page provides a summary of the steps Jahnke followed in doing paper chromatography. You will use a similar procedure as you do your own paper chromatography in Part 2 of this activity.

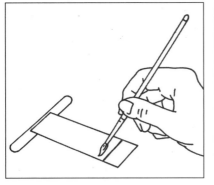

1. Jahnke painted a small sample of crushed microbial mat on a paper strip. She then allowed the strip to dry.

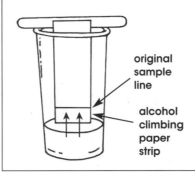

2. Jahnke submerged the tip of the paper strip in isopropyl alcohol. The alcohol began to climb up the strip as it was absorbed by the paper.

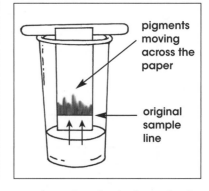

3. When the alcohol reached the microbial mat sample, it broke the sample into its chemical parts, called pigments. As the alcohol continued to climb, it carried the pigments along the paper.

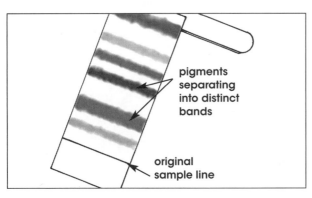

4. Some pigments moved across the paper more slowly than others. This caused the pigments to separate, creating distinct colored bands on the paper. Each colored band represented a different pigment.

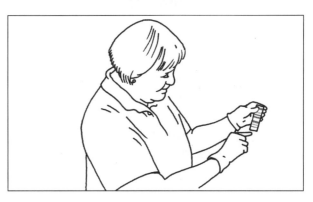

5. Jahnke analyzed the pattern of colored bands to determine the chemical makeup of the sample. This pattern is a type of chemical biosignature called a chromatogram.

ACTIVITY MASTER 3.3A

Chromatograms and Pigments

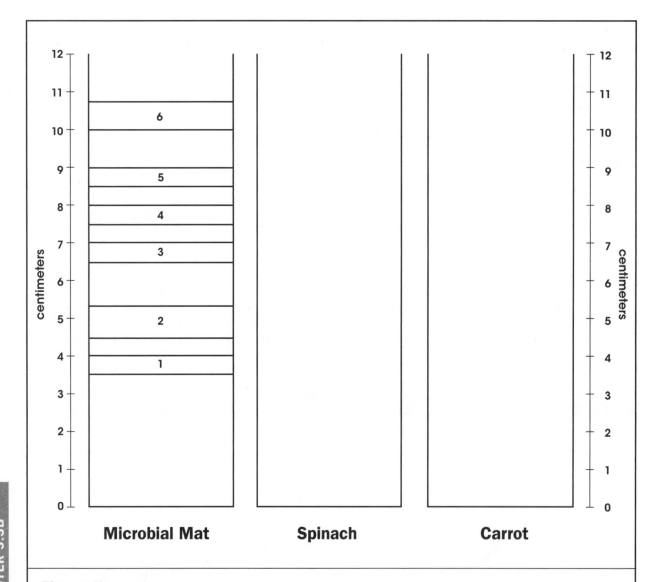

Microbial Mat   **Spinach**   **Carrot**

Pigment Key:

1. Deep Yellow: Carotenes (CARE oh teens)
2. Orange/Pink: Carotenes
3. Blue Green: Chlorophyll (KLOR oh fill)
4. Light Green: Chlorophyll
5. Yellow Green: Chlorophyll
6. Red/Orange: Carotenes

Notes:

- You might also see a light yellow pigment called xanthophyll (ZAN tho fill) in your chromatograms.
- Carotenes, chlorophylls, and xanthophylls are families of pigments.

©2006 JASON Foundation for Education

What's Living in Your Neighborhood?

BIG QUESTION

Why is it important to measure biotic and abiotic characteristics of an ecosystem

?

Focus Questions

1 What are biotic and abiotic characteristics in an ecosystem?

2 What are the "normal" ranges of life?

3 Are there "extremes" even in places that aren't extreme environments?

When you look out the window, what kinds of living things do you see? Maybe a squirrel is dashing across the street, or ants are building a hill in a sidewalk crack. If you took a walk by a local pond, you might see a whole other world of life: frogs croaking in the weeds, ducks dipping for their lunch, dragonflies skimming the water's surface. The area you live in is home to a variety of living things. But why do some things live along a city street and others in a pond?

1 What are biotic and abiotic characteristics in an ecosystem?

The plants, animals, and other living things in an environment are the **biotic** characteristics of the environment. *Biotic* means "pertaining to life." In order to understand the biotic characteristics of an environment, it is important to look at **abiotic** characteristics as well. *Abiotic* means "not living." Abiotic characteristics include sunlight, temperature, salinity, and pH.

Biotic and abiotic characteristics are closely linked in any **ecosystem**. An ecosystem is a community of living organisms, all interacting among themselves and with the environment in which they live. Through evolution, living things have adapted to particular abiotic conditions in particular ecosystems. Some species, such as humans, squirrels, and ants, are members of many different ecosystems. They have adapted to a wide range of abiotic conditions. Others, such as the extremophiles in hypersaline ponds or hot springs, have very specific abiotic requirements.

2 What are the "normal" ranges of life?

Most familiar living things live within a range of conditions people think of as normal. Studying extremophiles, however, has changed scientists' ideas about the limits of life. We now know that most species in the world are microorganisms that live outside of these so-called "normal" ranges.

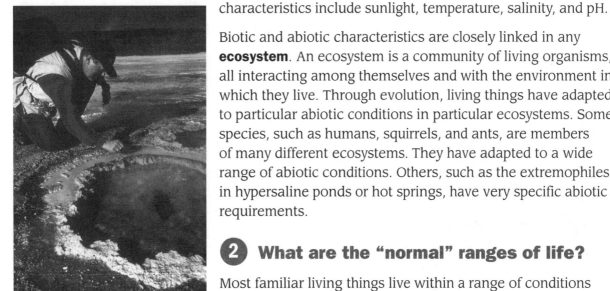

Jack Farmer explores a hot spring in Yellowstone National Park.

ARTICLE 3.4

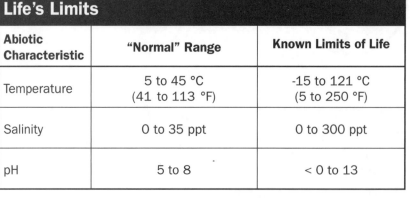

Life's Limits		
Abiotic Characteristic	**"Normal" Range**	**Known Limits of Life**
Temperature	5 to 45 °C (41 to 113 °F)	-15 to 121 °C (5 to 250 °F)
Salinity	0 to 35 ppt	0 to 300 ppt
pH	5 to 8	< 0 to 13

JASON host researchers Jack Farmer and Linda Jahnke have measured the abiotic characteristics of Mono Lake, Yellowstone's hot springs, and Guerrero Negro's ponds. They have used these data to understand the needs of the organisms they study. One of their first tasks was to establish a **baseline**, or set of starting measurements, for the abiotic characteristics in each environment. They can then compare the baseline with measurements taken at other times or from other sites. Establishing a baseline is important because every site is different. Baseline measurements of Yellowstone's boiling waters, for example, will probably be very different from those of a pond near your home. The baseline helps scientists understand what is "normal" for their sites.

③ Are there "extremes" even in places that aren't extreme environments?

Your aquatic field study site is probably not an extreme environment. But even an environment that is not extreme can go through drastic seasonal changes. In northern regions, winter can transform a mild lakeshore into an extreme of ice and snow. The life forms you observe in January would be very different from the ones you see in June. Many birds would have migrated, and insect and microscopic life might be **dormant**, or inactive. In summer, when heat dries up a pond, you would find different organisms than at the same pond in spring or fall.

Humans also alter environments in ways that make them more extreme. Pollution can change the pH of a stream or introduce chemicals harmful to organisms. A concrete expanse in a city center is an extreme environment where few species live. You might even find extreme environments in your own home or school. Can you think of local places that are extremely hot or cold, dark or light? Amazingly, there is probably life in those places!

This cityscape of asphalt, concrete, bricks, and glass is an extreme environment where few species live.

©2006 JASON Foundation for Education

ARTICLE 3.4

ACTIVITY 3.4

Local Field Investigation

Student Objectives

In this activity, you will:

- test the water at a local aquatic field site for salinity, temperature, and pH.
- identify vertebrate and invertebrate life forms.
- compare conditions at your aquatic site with those at extreme environments being studied by researchers Jack Farmer and Linda Jahnke.

In this activity, you are the field researcher! At a local site, you will be testing the waters for salinity, pH, temperature, and other properties, just like a real scientist. You will also discover what kinds of plants and animals live there. As you work, think about whether your environment has any extreme characteristics. You will have a chance to compare your results with data from Linda Jahnke and Jack Farmer when you get back to the classroom.

Materials

For each student

- plastic gloves
- safety goggles
- Activity Master 3.4A
- Activity Master 3.4B
- Activity Master 3.4C
- Baseline Study Form
- JASON Journal or additional blank paper
- pencil

For each group

- instructions, masters, and materials for the following Local Aquatic Field Study activities:
  - Air and Water Temperature
  - Measuring pH
  - Density and Salinity
  - Invertebrate Populations
- field guides for plants and animals
- hand lens and/or microscope

Procedure

Part 1: In the Field

1. Travel to your aquatic field study site. Find your group's quadrat along the shoreline. A quadrat is a rectangular area marked off for field studies.

2. On the Baseline Study Form, fill in the sections titled "Location Information" and "Study Site Profile." Use field guides, as necessary, to fill in plant and animal data.

3. Take biotic measurements of invertebrates in your quadrat by counting species and their numbers. Follow the procedures for the Invertebrate Populations activity. Use the Invertebrate Identification Sheet as a reference.

4. Take abiotic measurements in your quadrat. Follow the procedures for the Air and Water Temperature, Measuring pH, and Density and Salinity activities. Fill in the data on the Baseline Study Form. (You will not have data for all the tests on the form.)

©2006 JASON Foundation for Education

ACTIVITY 3.4

1. Construct a bar graph of the invertebrate populations (and any vertebrate populations) in your quadrat. List species on the horizontal axis (*x*-axis) and put population size on the vertical axis (*y*-axis). Then compile your class's data into a single bar graph.

2. Compile your class's abiotic data:

   a. Find the range, or span of all values recorded, for temperature, salinity, and pH.

   b. Find the median for each characteristic. The median is the exact middle measurement, above and below which lie an equal number of values.

   c. Calculate the mean, or average, for each characteristic.

3. Master 3.4A shows Jack Farmer's field data from Yellowstone's Grand Prismatic Hot Spring. The table contains temperature and pH data. Compare the range, median, and average values for temperature and pH at your site with those at the Grand Prismatic site.

4. Compare your class range, median, and average data values with Jack Farmer's field data from Mono Lake (Master 3.4B) and Linda Jahnke's data from Guerrero Negro (Master 3.4C).

5. Create a bar graph that shows the average pH for your site, Yellowstone's Grand Prismatic Hot Spring, Mono Lake, and Guerrero Negro's ponds. Create similar bar graphs to compare temperature and salinity data from the sites.

6. Use Team JASON Online to share your local site data with other schools.

Observations

1. What kinds of vertebrate, invertebrate, and plant life did you find in your quadrat?

2. What are the abiotic characteristics of your quadrat?

3. What are your class range, mean, and median values for temperature, salinity, and pH at your site?

4. What characteristics make Yellowstone's hot springs, Mono Lake, and Guerrero Negro's ponds extreme?

Conclusions

1. Was your site an extreme environment? Why or why not?

2. Were you surprised by the life you found at your site? Why or why not?

3. How does your local site's environment compare with the extreme environments studied by Linda Jahnke and Jack Farmer?

4. What have you learned to help answer the Big Question? In your JASON Journal, add information and summarize what you now know about the importance of measuring the biotic and abiotic characteristics of an ecosystem.

©2006 JASON Foundation for Education

Jack Farmer's Field Data for Yellowstone's Hot Springs

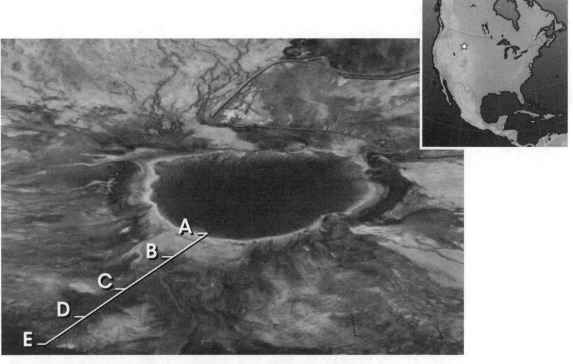

Jack Farmer's research site at Yellowstone National Park is the Grand Prismatic Spring, one of the world's largest hot springs. Farmer took the measurements in the table below along the straight line shown in the image above. The line ran from the edge of the spring along a channel flowing outward. Colonies of heat-loving bacteria thrive in the spring, in waters that top 70 °C (158 °F).

Temperature and pH Data for Yellowstone's Grand Prismatic Hot Spring					
Sample Site	A	B	C	D	E
Distance (m) from edge of hot spring	0	15.0	30.0	45.0	60.0
Temp (°C)	72	58	38	25	15
pH	7.8	8.0	8.3	8.6	8.6
Note: These hot spring waters have a low and, for the most part, uniform salinity, so it is not an important variable. Jack Farmer does not usually measure it.					

Jack Farmer's Field Data for Mono Lake

spring-fed marsh

E D C B A

stream channel

Jack Farmer's research site at Mono Lake is on the lake's western edge. Farmer took the measurements in the table below along a straight line that ran from a spring-fed marsh at the lake's edge, through a channel, and into the open lake. The measurements show that during the summer, the lake water's temperature, pH, and salinity are dramatically higher than the marsh water's.

Temperature, pH, and Salinity Data for Mono Lake

Sample Site	A	B	C	D	E
Distance (m) from marsh	0	2.0	4.0	6.0	8.0
Temp (°C)	13.0	15.0	24.0	25.0	25.0
pH	7.0	8.0	8.9	9.0	9.5
Salinity (ppt)	1.0	10.0	50.0	72.0	77.0

Linda Jahnke's Field Data for Guerrero Negro's Ponds

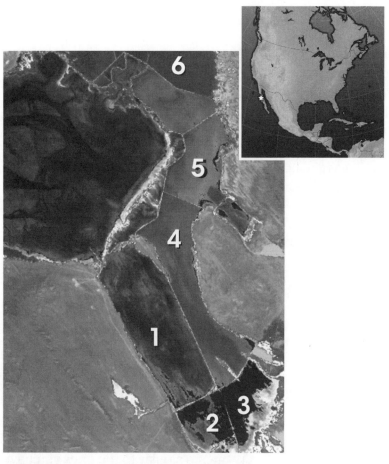

Linda Jahnke's research site at Guerrero Negro, Mexico, is a series of hypersaline ponds. These ponds are maintained for commercial salt production. Microbial mats are collected at Pond 4 for study in Jahnke's laboratory.

Temperature and Salinity Data for Guerrero Negro Ponds 3 through 6

Sample Site	Pond 3	Pond 4	Pond 5 near Pond 4	Pond 5 near Pond 6	Pond 6
Temp (°C)	17.0	16.0	16.3	17.0	16.3
Salinity (ppt)	69	93	101	107	111

Note: The pH at this site ranges from 8.1 to 9.

Mission Alert: Search for Life on Mars

Your Name: _____ **Date:** _____

National Astrobiology Center. You have been invited to join a group of scientists as they prepare for the first human mission to Mars to look for evidence of life. Your task is to prepare a mission plan that describes where on Mars you will look and why, what investigative methods you will use, and how you will test whatever clues you might find to determine whether life is or once was present.

Your Challenge

Investigate the problem and prepare a plan for your Mars mission to search for evidence of life. Use information from Unit 3, notes from your JASON Journal, and additional sources to prepare your plan.

Use the chart below to organize your work. Make sure you include the following:

1. The conditions necessary for life.
2. Where on Mars you might find those conditions.

3. What types of organisms might live there, and how you will look for evidence of life.

4. How you will use information from science experts, such as Jack Farmer and Linda Jahnke, in your mission. This information should include descriptions of the tools and methods they use in their studies and the results of their research on life in extreme environments.

5. Your plan to prove that life was once present, should you find some interesting clues during the Mars mission.

Conclusions

Based on your information:

- Where on Mars should you look for evidence of life?
- How could you prove that the signatures you might find are evidence of life?
- Where on Earth might you find environments similar to the ones you have decided to study on Mars?

Your "To Do" List: Use the table below to organize your work.

Task	Sources	Graphics (Yes/No)	Completed (Yes/No)
Identified conditions necessary for life			
Determined where on Mars those locations might exist			
Hypothesized types of organisms that might live on Mars; described how to study them			
Summarized study methods and gathered data on life in extreme environments			

©2006 JASON Foundation for Education

Appendix A
The Scientist's Toolbox

This toolbox provides background information on writing a scientific report, making and converting measurements, using scientific notation, and understanding electromagnetic radiation. You may find the following information helpful as you read the JASON curriculum.

The Scientific Method: Tips on Writing a Scientific Report

You may be asked to write reports about what you learn from doing activities in the JASON curriculum. A scientific report should follow a specific format.

Research question: State the research question that you will be investigating.

Hypothesis: State your expected answer to the research question. This expected answer is your hypothesis: "I think . . ."

Materials: Provide details about the materials you will need to perform your investigation.

Procedure: Describe the step-by-step procedure you will use in your investigation. Be sure to provide enough details so that somebody else could use your procedure to do the investigation.

Results: Explain the results of your investigation. If possible, design data tables and graphs to present your results. Analyze your data and provide summary information, such as the range and mean of the data.

Conclusion: State whether or not your hypothesis was supported. Then explain your findings to answer the question you asked earlier. Begin your conclusion with a summarizing statement, such as "I found that..."

Measurements

Good measurements are essential to good science, so you'll need to know how to make measurements and how to convert between the English system and the metric system. The measurements used in the *Mysteries of Earth and Mars* curriculum include measures of length, mass, volume, area, and temperature. They are shown in the text in metric system units, with the English system equivalent in parentheses. Here are some of the metric units you need to know.

Measurement	Metric Unit	Unit Abbreviation
Length	meter, kilometer	m, km
Mass	gram, kilogram	g, kg
Volume	milliliter, liter, cubic centimeter	mL, L, cm^3
Area	square meter, square kilometer	m^2, km^2
Temperature	degree Celsius	°C

Conversion Procedures

Because people may use either the metric system or the English system for measurement, you need to be able to convert from one system to the other in order to share information. Sharing data is important in science. Just think about what might happen if two groups working on a project used different systems of measurement and could not share their data because they could not convert their measurements from one system to the other.

Conversion Table

	Conversion Factors						
Length	**in.**	**ft**	**mi**	**n.m.**	**cm**	**m**	**km**
Inch (in.)	1.0	0.083	0.0000158	0.0000137	2.54	0.0254	0.0000254
Foot (ft)	12.0	1.0	0.0001893	0.000164	30.48	0.3048	0.0003048
Mile (mi)	63,360	5280	1.0	0.86956	160,934.4	1609.344	1.609344
Nautical mile (n.m.)	72,913	6076	1.15	1.0	185,200	1852	1.852
Centimeter (cm)	0.3937	0.0328	0.0000062	0.0000053	1.0	0.01	0.00001
Meter (m)	39.37	3.2808	0.0006214	0.00053	100	1.0	0.001
Kilometer (km)	39,370	3280.8	0.6213712	0.53	100,000	1000	1.0
Area	**A**	**ha**	**km²**				
Acre (A)	1.0	0.4047	0.004047				
Hectare (ha)	2.47114	1.0	0.01				
Square kilometer (km²)	247.114	100	1.0				
Volume	**qt**	**gal**	**L**				
Quart (qt)	1.0	0.25	0.946				
Gallon (gal)	4.0	1.0	3.785				
Liter (L)	1.06	0.264	1.0				
Mass and Weight	**oz**	**lb**	**g**	**kg**			
Ounce (oz)	1.0	0.0625	28.35	0.02835			
Pound (lb)	16.0	1.0	453.6	0.4536			
Gram (g)	0.0353	0.00220	1.0	0.0001			
Kilogram (kg)	35.2	2.2	1000.0	1.0			
Temperature	**°F**	**°C**					
Degree Fahrenheit (°F)	n/a	(°F − 32) ÷1.8					
Degree Celsius (°C)	(1.8 x °C) + 32	n/a					

The table above gives the conversion factors you should use if you need to convert measurements. Let's say you want to convert a metric unit of measure to an English unit of measure. To use the table, find the row for the metric unit on the left side of the table. Next, find the column for the English unit at the top of the table. The number in the cell where the row and column intersect is the one you need to multiply by to make the conversion. You can also use the table to convert from an English unit of measure to a metric unit of measure.

Here's an example: The length of a standard sheet of paper is 11 inches. If you wanted to convert 11 inches to centimeters, you would look at the row for inches and at the column for centimeters. Since the intersection of the row and column on the table shows that the conversion factor is 2.54, you would multiply 11 by 2.54 and get 27.94. This means that 11 inches is equivalent to 27.94 centimeters. You should note that the metric/English conversions in the *Mysteries of Earth and Mars* text have been rounded to maintain the same number of significant digits. Thus, the text will say that the length of a standard sheet of paper is 28 centimeters.

Temperature conversions are slightly different. You must use an algebraic formula to convert between the two sets of temperature units.

Electromagnetic Spectrum

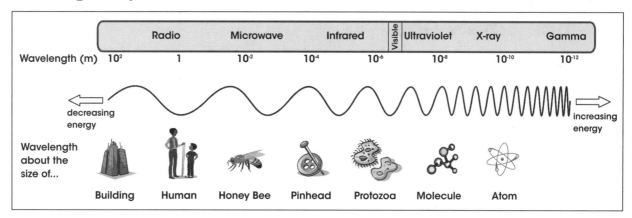

Scientific Notation

Scientific notation is a method used to simplify the writing of very large and very small numbers. When a number is written in scientific notation, it is separated into two parts: a coefficient and a power of 10. The coefficient is a number between 1 and 10. The power of 10 is 10 with an exponent that represents how many places the decimal point in the coefficient should be moved to the right or to the left. A positive exponent indicates that the decimal point should be moved to the right. A negative exponent indicates that the decimal point should be moved to the left. For example, the Sun is 93 million miles from Earth. In scientific notation, 93,000,000 miles would be written as 9.3×10^7 miles. The coefficient is 9.3 and the power to which 10 is raised is the exponent 7. Thus, the decimal point in the coefficient should be moved 7 places to the right. Bacteria are generally about 0.000005 meter long. In scientific notation, this number would be written as 5×10^{-6} meter. The coefficient is 5 and the power of 10 is -6. The decimal point in the coefficient, understood to be after the 5, should be moved 6 places to the left.

Here are some examples of powers of 10 applied to the coefficient 3:

$10^1 = 10$	$3 \times 10^1 = 30$	$10^{-1} = 0.1$	$3 \times 10^{-1} = 0.3$
$10^2 = 100$	$3 \times 10^2 = 300$	$10^{-2} = 0.01$	$3 \times 10^{-2} = 0.03$
$10^3 = 1000$	$3 \times 10^3 = 3000$	$10^{-3} = 0.001$	$3 \times 10^{-3} = 0.003$

Electromagnetic Radiation

Electromagnetic radiation is energy that travels through space in the form of waves. Electromagnetic radiation comes in different forms such as radio waves, visible light, and X-rays. The Sun constantly radiates all forms of electromagnetic radiation, including infrared radiation that you feel as heat, visible light that you see, and ultraviolet radiation that can give you a sunburn. All of the radiation from the Sun travels the 93 million miles to Earth in 8 minutes. This is because all forms of electromagnetic radiation travel at the same speed: 3.0×10^8 m/s (9.8×10^8 ft/s).

The **electromagnetic spectrum** is a system that classifies the different forms of electromagnetic radiation according to wavelength. The length of a wave corresponds to how much energy the wave carries. For example, radio waves have long wavelengths and carry low energy. X-rays have short wavelengths and carry high energy. The electromagnetic spectrum spans the entire range of wavelengths for all forms of electromagnetic radiation.

The entire electromagnetic spectrum is very useful in scientific research. Although visible light is only a tiny portion of the electromagnetic spectrum, special instruments enable scientists to "see" and study other forms of radiation as well. Studying how different forms of radiation interact with objects can help scientists learn more about the structure and chemical composition of the objects.

Appendix B
Science Safety Tips

One of the first things you will learn as a beginning scientist is that working in the classroom, in the laboratory, or at a field site can be an exciting experience. Doing hands-on activities can help you discover the wonders of science. But as in any activity, science experiences require planning, caution, and common sense for your safety and that of others.

To better understand the concepts in the JASON curriculum, you will probably do many activities. If you follow instructions and are careful, your experiences will be successful and rewarding.

Read the safety tips below carefully and try to remember them whenever you are working in the laboratory or at a field site.

1. Follow your teacher's directions or the activity's directions carefully.

2. Whenever you are unsure of a particular step in an activity, ask your teacher for help.

3. Wash your hands before and after doing an activity.

4. Always maintain a clean work area.

5. Never eat or drink at your work area.

6. Handle glassware safely. Never use broken or chipped glassware. Watch for hot glassware.

7. Never heat anything unless instructed to do so. Use only candles or approved hot plates for heating.

8. Always be aware of whether the chemicals you are working with are hazardous. Because many chemicals can be hazardous, handle all of them carefully.

9. Never smell any chemical directly from its container. If instructed to smell a chemical, use your hand to waft some of the odors from the top of the chemical container toward your nose.

10. NEVER taste a chemical (in this lab context).

11. Wear safety glasses whenever working with chemicals, heat, flames, or anything that can shatter or fly.

12. Handle all sharp instruments with extreme care.

13. Collect soils only from unpolluted and uncontaminated areas. Wear disposable gloves if there is any question. Make sure you have permission to collect soils from the locations you choose.

14. Never cause pain, discomfort, or injury to an animal. Stay away from wild animals, living or dead.

15. Follow your teacher's directions when handling live animals.

16. Notify your teacher immediately if you cut or burn yourself, or if you spill a chemical on yourself.

17. Dispose of all materials according to your teacher's directions. Clean up your work area and return equipment to its proper place.

©2006 JASON Foundation for Education

Appendix C
Glossary

abiotic not living

accelerate (ak SELL uh rate) to change the velocity of an object over time

acidic (uh SIH dik) property of having a low pH, or high concentration of hydrogen ions

aerobrake (AIR oh BRAYK) to slow a spacecraft using the friction generated by the passage of the craft through a planet's atmosphere

alkaline property of having a high pH, or low concentration of hydrogen ions

alloy a material made from a mixture of other materials, typically metals; can have very different properties from the original materials used to create it

analog (AN uh log) a real-life model that is similar to something else but somewhat different in structure, composition, and/or origin

asteroid belt a band of thousands of small rocky and metallic objects in orbit around the Sun; the region of space between the orbits of Mars and Jupiter

astrobiology (AS troh by AHL uh jee) the study of life in the universe, including the development of life on Earth and the search for life on other planets

atmosphere a mixture of gases that surrounds a planet

atmospheric pressure the force on an object's surface due to the weight of the atmosphere above it

axis an imaginary line about which a planet rotates

baseline a set of starting measurements that provide a basis for comparison with later measurements

biosignature a sign of present or past life

biotic living or pertaining to life

boiling point the temperature at which a substance changes state from a liquid to a gas

caldera a large, circular pit at the top of a volcano that is formed when the volcano explodes or collapses; a volcanic crater

canyon a deep, narrow valley that has steep sides

channel a long, narrow path cut by a natural process (such as running water) or an artificial process (such as digging)

chemosynthesis (KEE moh SIN thuh sis) the process by which living things use chemicals from the environment to create energy

chromatography (kroh muh TAH gruh fee) the method in which a chemical mixture is passed through a material that separates it into its chemical parts, leaving a unique biosignature

controls factors that are kept the same throughout an investigation

cosmic radiation high-energy particles that are emitted by the Sun and other objects in space; can be harmful to human health

cratering the geological process that produces bowl-shaped pits, or craters, on a planet's surface

cyanobacteria (SY uh noh bak TEER ee uh) a single-celled microorganism that can live in a variety of extreme conditions

data pieces of information that are collected during an investigation

dependent variable a factor that is measured to see how it changes in response to changes in the independent variable of an investigation

dormant inactive

ecosystem a community of living organisms, interacting among themselves and with their environment

ejecta crushed rock fragments and other material thrown in all directions when an impact crater is formed

electromagnetic radiation energy that travels through space in the form of electromagnetic waves

emissivity (ee mih SIV uh tee) a measure of how much radiation an object gives off at a particular wavelength

energy the ability to do work; exists in forms such as motion, light, heat, sound, and electricity

energy transfer the change of energy from one form to another

erosion the wearing away of a planet's surface by natural forces such as wind, gravity, ice, and moving water

extreme environment a place where conditions are at the outer limits of the ranges in which life can survive

extremophile (ik STREE muh file) an organism that thrives in extreme environments

food chain a method of tracking how energy passes from one organism to another

force a push or a pull that acts on an object

fossil the traces or remains of a living organism from the past, usually preserved in rock

freezing point the temperature at which a substance changes state from a liquid to a solid

friction a force that resists the motion between two surfaces in contact

geology the study of the history, structure, and composition of Earth and other rocky planets

gravity the force of attraction between any two objects; depends on the masses of the objects and the distance between them

hardness the measure of a mineral's resistance to scratching or cutting

hypersaline (HY puhr SAY leen) extremely salty

hypothesis an initial, testable explanation of an observation; an attempt to answer a research question before conducting an investigation

igneous a type of rock that forms from hot, melted rock material that cools and becomes solid

impact crater a bowl-shaped pit on the surface of a planet formed when an impactor crashes into the ground

©2006 JASON Foundation for Education

impactor a rock from space which is large enough and traveling fast enough to form a crater when it hits the surface of a planet

independent variable the factor that is varied in an investigation

infrared (in fruh RED) **radiation** radiation with wavelengths longer than visible light waves but shorter than microwaves

kinetic energy the energy of motion

lava flow masses of melted rock that pour onto the surface of a planet during a volcanic eruption; the resulting smooth surface of solidified lava

Martian meteorite a rock from Mars that has traveled through space and landed on Earth

Martian soil simulant soil that is made from materials on Earth but that looks similar to soil on Mars

melting point the temperature at which a substance changes state from a solid to a liquid

metamorphic a type of rock that forms when high temperatures and pressures cause igneous rocks or sedimentary rocks to change form

microbial mat a thick, spongy formation made of layers of microorganisms

microbiologist a person who studies forms of life that can be seen only through a microscope

micron (MY krahn) a distance equal to one millionth of a meter (10^{-6} m); also known as a micrometer

microorganism a living thing so small that it can be seen only with a microscope

mineral a natural, inorganic, solid substance that has a unique atomic structure and characteristic physical and chemical properties

molten rock rock that is in liquid form

mountain a high point of land rising steeply above its surroundings

nutrients (NOO tree uhnts) vitamins, minerals, and other raw materials that all living things need to live and grow

orbit a circular or elliptical path around a planet or star

organic matter plant or animal material, either living or dead

phase change the change from one physical state (such as liquid, solid, or gas) to another

photosynthesis (foh toh SIN thuh sis) the process by which living things use sunlight as an energy source to make nutrients such as sugars

plate a thick slab of rock that forms part of the crust of a planet

plate tectonics the theory that Earth's surface is made of many different plates that have moved throughout geological time resulting in the present-day positions of the continents, the formation of mountains and volcanoes, and the production of earthquakes

potential energy stored energy

Principle of Cross-Cutting Relationships principle which states that younger geological features cut across older geological features

Principle of Superposition principle which states that younger geological features are on top of older geological features

 Q

qualitative observation description of a quality such as shape, color, odor, texture, or behavior

quantitative observation numerical measurement of a quantity such as length, mass, temperature, or volume

 R

radiation energy that travels through space in the form of waves

research question the guiding question for an investigation

rim the raised ring around a crater bowl that forms from the ejecta that piles up there

rock a hard, solid, natural material that is made up of one or more minerals

 S

scale factor a constant multiplier that converts a measurement from one size to another

scientific notation a method used to simplify the writing of very large and very small numbers; a number written in scientific notation is expressed as a coefficient between 1 and 10 multiplied by a power of 10

sedimentary a type of rock that forms when rock or mineral fragments are compressed or cemented into solid layers

soil the layer of loose material on a planet's surface; can contain rock fragments, organic material, water, and air

sol a Martian day; the time it takes for Mars to rotate once (24 hr, 39 min)

solar energy energy from the Sun

solar system the collection of objects in orbit around a star

spectrometer (spek TRAH muh tuhr) an instrument for recording the spectrum of an object by measuring how much radiation comes from the object over a range of wavelengths

spectrum (plural: spectra) a graph of the intensity of radiation given off by an object at different wavelengths

streak the color of a mineral in its powdered form; this color is obtained by rubbing the mineral across a hard, rough surface and observing the mark it leaves

 T

tectonics (tek TAH nics) the study of how a planet's crust moves, folds, and cracks

 V

volcanism the geological process related to the eruption of lava, rock fragments, and gases at a planet's crust

volcano an opening in a planet's crust through which gases, lava, and hot ashes erupt; the mountain or hill built up by the lava and ash

 W

wavelength the distance between two consecutive peaks, troughs, or other identical parts of a wave

Credits

In addition to those people listed at the front of this book, we'd like to acknowledge the many people who have each played a role in the development of the JASON Expedition: Mysteries of Earth and Mars *curriculum*.

Host Researchers

Kobie T. Boykins, *Cognizant Mechanical Engineer, Mars Exploration Rovers, NASA Jet Propulsion Laboratory, CA*

Tracy D. Drain, *Systems Engineer, Mars Reconnaissance Orbiter Project, NASA Jet Propulsion Laboratory, CA*

Jack D. Farmer, Ph.D., *Professor, Dept. of Geological Sciences, Arizona State University, AZ*

James B. Garvin, Ph.D., *NASA Chief Scientist, NASA Headquarters, Washington, DC*

Victoria E. Hamilton, Ph.D., *Assistant Professor, Hawai'i Institute of Geophysics and Planetology, University of Hawai'i*

Linda Jahnke, *Research Scientist (Assistant Chief, Exobiology Branch), Space Science and Astrobiology Division, Science Directorate, NASA Ames Research Center, CA*

Guest Researcher

Allan Treiman, Ph.D., *Senior Staff Scientist, Lunar and Planetary Institute, Houston, TX*

Student Hosts

Mitchell Graves, *Student, Embry-Riddle Aeronautical University, FL*

Katie Keller, *Student, Virginia Polytechnic Institute and State University, VA*

Jeff Meng, *Student, University of Michigan, MI*

Curriculum Review Team

JASON Host Researchers, along with:

Laura Batt, *JFE*; Ben Carlisle, *JFE*; James Russell Carpenter, *NASA Goddard Space Flight Center*; Francesca Casella, *JFE*; Pamela Gales Conrad, *NASA Jet Propulsion Laboratory*; Michael DiSpezio, *JFE*; Pam Hirschfeld, *Brown Publishing Network*; Katie James, *JFE*; Caroline Joyce, *JFE*; Sheri Klug, *Arizona State University Mars Education Program*; Heidi L. K. Manning, *Associate Professor of Physics, Concordia College*; Scott Ness, *NASA Goddard Space Flight Center*; Henry Olds, *JFE*; Haris Papamichael, *JFE*; Elsie Rivard, *JFE*; Sherry Shanihan, *JFE*; Josh Sheldon, *JFE*; Sallie M. Smith, *NASA Goddard Space Flight Center*; Gary Standafer, *JFE*; Michelle Viotti, *NASA Jet Propulsion Laboratory*.

Field Testers

Mary Cahill, *The Potomac School, McLean, VA*

Kim Castagna, *Canalino Elementary School, Carpinteria, CA*

Ellen Dailey, *Newman Elementary School, Needham, MA*

Tom Fitzpatrick, *Breckinridge Middle School, Roanoke, VA*

Mary Lavin, *Plymouth Community Intermediate School, Plymouth, MA*

Katie Mahoney, *Pollard Middle School, Needham, MA*

Joseph Marino, *Newman Elementary School, Needham, MA*

Bruce McCandless, *Berea Middle School, Greenville, SC*

Dee McLellan, *Meadow Creek Christian School, Andover, MN*

Pam Schmidt, *Thunder Ridge Middle School, Aurora, CO*

Carla-Rae Smith, *Jackson Middle School, Champlin, MN*

Literature Selection Team

Michele Bouchard, *JASON Foundation for Education*

Beth Carnes, *Rogers Public Schools, Rogers, AR*

Betsy Fried, *Toledo-Lucas County Public Library, Toledo, OH*

Holly Garrett, *Endurfything Ontario, Inc., Ancaster, ON*

Mary Mendoza, *Col. John O. Ensor Middle School, El Paso, TX*

Jean Monahan, *JASON Foundation for Education*

Kim Rado, *Aurora School, Cuyahoga Falls, OH*

Dr. Jan Woerner, *UCSB-Palm Desert, Palm Desert, CA*

Special Thanks

Jackie Allen, *NASA Johnson Space Center, Houston, TX*

Steven Allison-Bunnell, *Educational Web Adventures, St. Paul, MN*

Bruce Banerdt, *NASA Jet Propulsion Laboratory, CA*

Mary Cahill, *The Potomac School, McLean, VA*

Emilie Condon, *Sherwood Githens Middle School, Durham, NC*

Michael Dubie, *Data Associates, Waltham, MA*

Louis Estey, *UNAVCO, Boulder, CO*

Anthony Fisher, *Brown Publishing Network, Waltham, MA*

Reesa Fischer, *JASON Foundation for Education*

Darlene Foley, *Data Associates, Waltham, MA*

Ilana Hardesty, *JASON Foundation for Education*

©2006 JASON Foundation for Education

Photo and Art Credits

Photography

Copyright 1995, Ron Baalke
pg 68 (top left)

Courtesy of J. Beck, NASA/JPL
pg 48 (top right)

Courtesy of R. Bouchard, NASA
pg 13 (left), 48 (top left), 61 (top)

Cartesia/pdgr008386/Getty Images
pg 109 (right), 110 (right), 111 (right)

Data courtesy of MGS/MOLA; mapping tools courtesy of UNAVCO/Jules Verne Map Server, Web site: http://jules.unavco.org
pg 57

Courtesy of T. Drain
pg 20 (top right)

Courtesy of J. Farmer
pg 14 (left), 82 (top left), 93, 109 (left), 110 (left)

Alfred Gescheldt/The Image Bank/Getty Images
pg 106

Courtesy of V. Hamilton
pg 68 (bottom)

Linda Jahnke
pg 101, 111 (left)

Katie James
pg 5 (top)

Lowell Observatory Archives
pg 84

Michael Milstein
pg 82 (top right), 105

Courtesy of NASA and the Lunar & Planetary Institute
pg 42

NASA
pg 22 (top), 26, 29, 50 (top), 84 (top), 85, 94, 100

NASA/JPL
pg 12–17 (background), 22 (middle and bottom), 32, 37 (middle and bottom), 39, 47, 75, 88, 92, 118–123 (background)

NASA/JPL/Cornell
pg 3–5 (background), 6 (left), 6–11 (background), 18–19 (background), 30, 36, 113–117 (background)

NASA/JPL/Malin Space Science Systems
pg 41, 53 (bottom), 60, 62 (top), 76 (top), 81

NASA Kennedy Space Center
pg 24

NASA/MOLA Science Team
pg 11

NASA/MOLA Science Team/USGS Astrogeology Research Program
pg 50 (bottom), 58, 59, 65

Courtesy of D. Roddy, USGS Astrogeology Research Program
pg 62 (middle)

Daniel J. Splaine Photography
Cover, pg 1, pg 6 (right), 12, 13 (right), 14 (right), 15, 16, 20 (top left; bottom left and right), 31, 37 (top), 38, 46, 48 (bottom left and right), 67 (top), 78, 80, 82 (bottom left and right), 99 (top and bottom), 112

USGS
pg 53 (middle)

Andrew Ward/Life File/Getty Images
pg 99 (middle)

Courtesy of D. Williams and J. Friedlander, NSSDC
pg 62 (bottom)

Illustrations

Jean Cassels
pg 25, 76 (bottom), 86, 87, 96, 103

Andrea Golden
pg 23, 35, 42

Greg Harris
pg 33, 52, 53 (top), 72–73

Lynne Hogan, Electronic Data Systems
pg 18, 124

Earl Misquitta
pg 7

Based on an image from NASA: Imagine the Universe!
pg 115 (top)

NOTES

NOTES

NOTES

NOTES

JASON EXPEDITION:
Mysteries of Earth and Mars

Teachers—

Now *you can provide your students with their own copies of this attractive book!*

- *An affordable alternative to photocopying*
- *Vivid color and images throughout*
- *A valuable resource that is theirs to keep*

Order *additional copies of this Student Activities Book for your students today!*

Order Form:

	Quantity	Price	Total
JASON Expedition: Mysteries of Earth and Mars Student Activities Books - Set of 10 books		$60.00	
Shipping & Handling (Per set of 10 books)		$15.00	
		TOTAL	

Ship to:

Contact Name: _____

School/Org: _____

Mailing Address: _____

City: _____ State: _____ Zip: _____ Country: _____

Phone: _____ Fax: _____ E-mail: _____

Bill to *(if different from above)*:

Contact Name: _____

School/Org: _____

Mailing Address: _____

City: _____ State: _____ Zip: _____ Country: _____

Phone: _____ Fax: _____ E-mail: _____

Payment:

☐ Check Payable to: JASON Foundation for Education ☐ Purchase Order #: _____

☐ Mastercard ☐ VISA ☐ American Express

Card Number: _____ Exp. Date: _____

Cardholder's Name: _____

Cardholder's Signature: _____

Please send completed order forms via FAX: **781-444-8313**

Or mail to: **JASON Foundation for Education**
11 Second Avenue
Needham Heights, MA 02494

Order Online: **http://store.jason.org**